CONTENT

Content

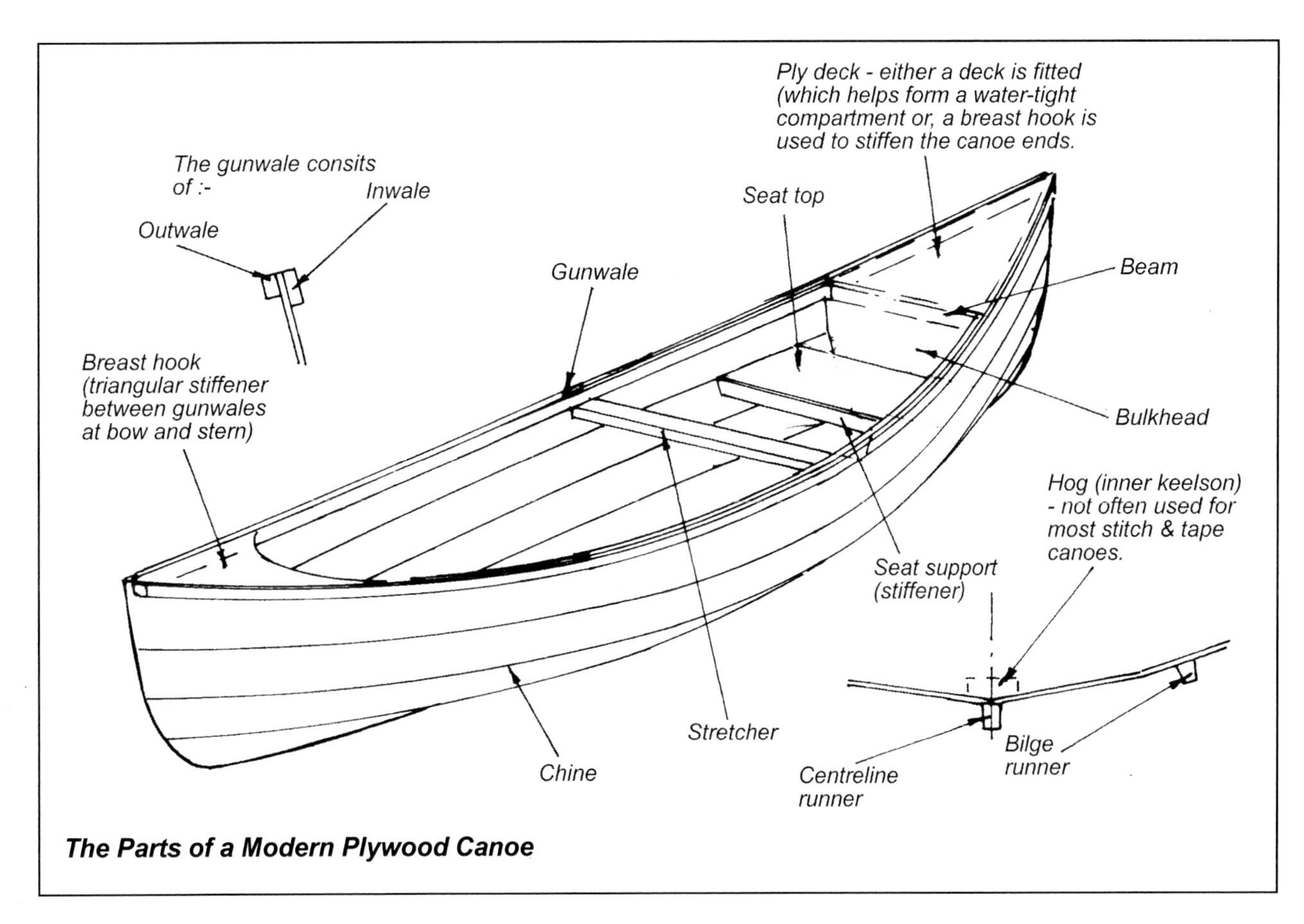

The Parts of a Modern Plywood Canoe

A Quick Summary of the Stitch & Tape Canoe Building Process covered in this Manual

Left, the plywood planks for this Christine 13'9" open canoe are longer than a standard sheet of plywood and are therefore being joined using a simple glass tape butt join.

Right—the same planks being stitched together—the first two pairs are in place. The weights are simply preventing the planks from trying to fold up along the centre.

Left, the third pair of planks have been stitched in place and the shape is beginning to look like a canoe—at this stage the stitches are kept loose.

Right, the finished canoe on Roadford Lake in Cornwall—total building time up to the point of painting and finishing was 45 hours—that's two weekends plus some evenings.

INTRODUCTION

THE MODERN METHOD OF PLY CANOE CONSTRUCTION

Plywood is an ideal material to use in building a canoe - it is available in large sheets (trees do not yield up their timber in sheet form), these large sheets are stable, relatively light in weight for their strength and stiffness and cheap (in the non-Marine grades which I use for canoe building). Also, the bi-directional laminates of plywood, mean that the ply is strong both along and across it's length (unlike timber which is very strong along it's length and weak across it's grain direction). Finally, it is easily cut and glued.

Linking these and other advantages to those imparted by epoxies (high strength, ease of application/low construction time etc) means that amateur built ply canoes can now be built quickly and will be very durable. The conventional way of building a ply canoe consisted of first constructing a fairly heavy timber framework which included frames, stringers and hog/keel, stem and stern posts. The ply was then applied to the framework very much as a skin simply to keep the water out and in many cases the additional strength given to the structure by the ply was not taken into account (Figure 1).

One advantage of this method, which is called 'ply-on- frame' construction, is that very often, the ply panels are put on over-size (except where they meet at chines) and trimmed to shape after the glue has dried, making skinning the canoe quite simple. However, with it's framework, the canoe is often much heavier than it needs to be, is expensive and takes a long time to build.

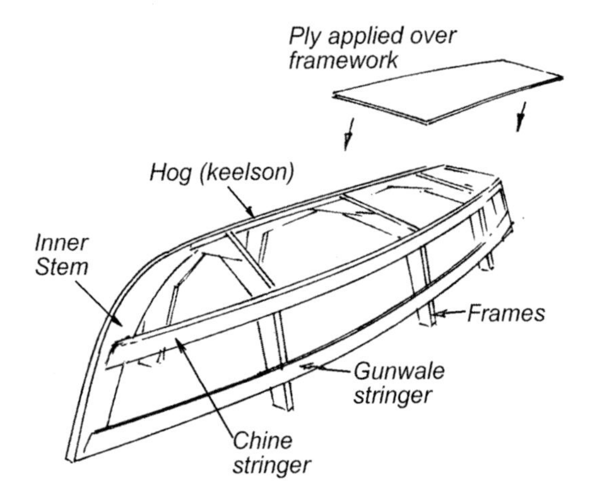

Fig 1. Ply over frame construction.

When you put a bend into plywood, it becomes very stiff and if you can use this property and at the same time, simply lock the joints between ply panels together with glue, rather than a solid wood structure, you will be able to produce a boat which is light, stiff, quicker to build and lower in cost than a conventional 'ply-on-frame' canoe.

This is where the Barry Bucknall (although others have claimed to be the first to develop it) stitch and tape technology came in. One of the first boats to use this method of construction, which uses pre-shaped ply hull panels joined edge to edge by fibreglass tape, was the Mirror 11 pram dinghy. The art of boat building then becomes similar to that of dress making or sail making where the shapes of the cloth panels are cut on the flat and when stitched together, the curves cut into the panel edges force 3-dimensional curvature into the ply hull shape. Stitch and tape is also known as 'tack and glue', 'stitch and glue' and 'tack and tape'.

In the conventional 'ply-on-frame' method of construction, we are working from the 'inside-out' whereas, with modern stitch and tape construction, we are working from 'outside-in' – marking and cutting the plywood plank shapes out first (from patterns/dimensions given on the plans), stitching these together along their mating edges (chines) and then pushing any ply bulkheads/dividers into place before finishing and sealing the chine seams etc with epoxy and glass tape—***see Page 4 for the initial stages in the construction of a stitch and tape Christine canoe.***

I have designed over 60 canoes and built many of them using the stitch and tape method with cheap Exterior Grade plywood and ordinary joinery grade Deal (White Pine) and finished them with exterior quality household paints and varnishes. These canoe have lasted me many years and have, at a low cost, given me many hours of pleasure both in their construction and use. If they get dropped or scratched or badly abused, the fact that they were cheap to make and took few skills and little time to build, means that I am not worried – a fresh overcoat of paint is all that is required every couple of years or so to keep them looking smart.

In all the boat building and boating I have done over the years, I have never had more pleasure per unit cost than I have had with a stitch and tape canoe. I hope that this book inspires you to take up a saw and build a canoe for yourself.

Paul Fisher
2009

Chapter 1

TOOLS, SKILLS & THE WORKSHOP

1.1 The Work Area

First of all, let me say, that my idea of canoe building, is to build a craft as efficiently as possible from the point of view of time and cost. If you are using a modern design, and the designer has done his job correctly, there should be no need for large work areas or a large collection of expensive tools.

I built my first canoe as a schoolboy in the school workshops. Having proudly completed the craft and lovingly applied the final coat of varnish to the coaming and other bright work, we discovered, to our intense embarrassment, that we could not remove the canoe from the workshop. The door was large enough with the canoe on it's side, but there was a fixed corridor outside that was close enough to prevent us from turning the corner.

What we thought were large enough windows on the other side of the workshop, turned out to be too small until finally, we had to remove the coaming to get the boat through. The lesson is of course, a very simple one. Check, to make sure that you can get your canoe out of the work area without having to chop it in half or remove a wall!

For ply/epoxy or tape construction, dry conditions are a must and in order for the glues and more especially, the polyester or epoxy resins to cure, a warm atmosphere is also required.

Another must, is a good working light. Poor lighting conditions help hide all sorts of nasties and apart from not doing your own eyes any good, such conditions will not allow you to eye up the canoe at the critical stage, when all the hull panels have been stitched together, to make sure that your canoe is fair and untwisted.

A good point about modern ply canoe construction is that we are not talking about a long term project. We are, in fact looking at perhaps just 30 to 50 hours of work for one person to get the project to the painting stage. For many of the Selway Fisher canoes, this would include marking and cutting out the ply panels, and therefore, it is quite possible to make a canoe in an area normally used for other purposes. But be warned, consult your nearest and dearest first - I do not want to be cited in any divorce cases!

The ideal minimum length for the work area, would be around 6' longer than the canoe, so that you can get around each end of the canoe easily and so that there is enough length for the storage of long wood stock (gunwale, stringers etc).

To mark the hull panel shapes onto the 8'x4' (1220x2440mm) ply panels, you will need room to lay the sheets down and to manoeuvre them around. Therefore, a work area width of at least 8' (2.44m) is required and more if possible taking into account the need for space for at least a Workmate (collapsable bench/vice) if not some sort of bench (Figure 2).

Now, having said all this, I have built canoes in far from ideal conditions where room has been extremely tight and where the canoe has had to be made in 2 halves and glued together later outside the work area. Light, at times has come from a single bulb slung over a rafter, rather than a couple of 6' (1.8m) fluorescent tubes which I feel are the ideal, and where temperatures required the personal use of 3 layers of jumpers, 2 shirts and thermal socks!

After many years of building boats in such far from ideal conditions, the very least that I now insist upon, is a good light source overhead, with another that I can move around, a clean environment which can be easily swept down at the end of each building session, and the ability to use at least a portable heat source which, in combination with some plastic sheet draped over the canoe, will build up a warm environment around the boat for curing the glues and resins. Taking all this into account, the standard modern garage is usually quite adequate.

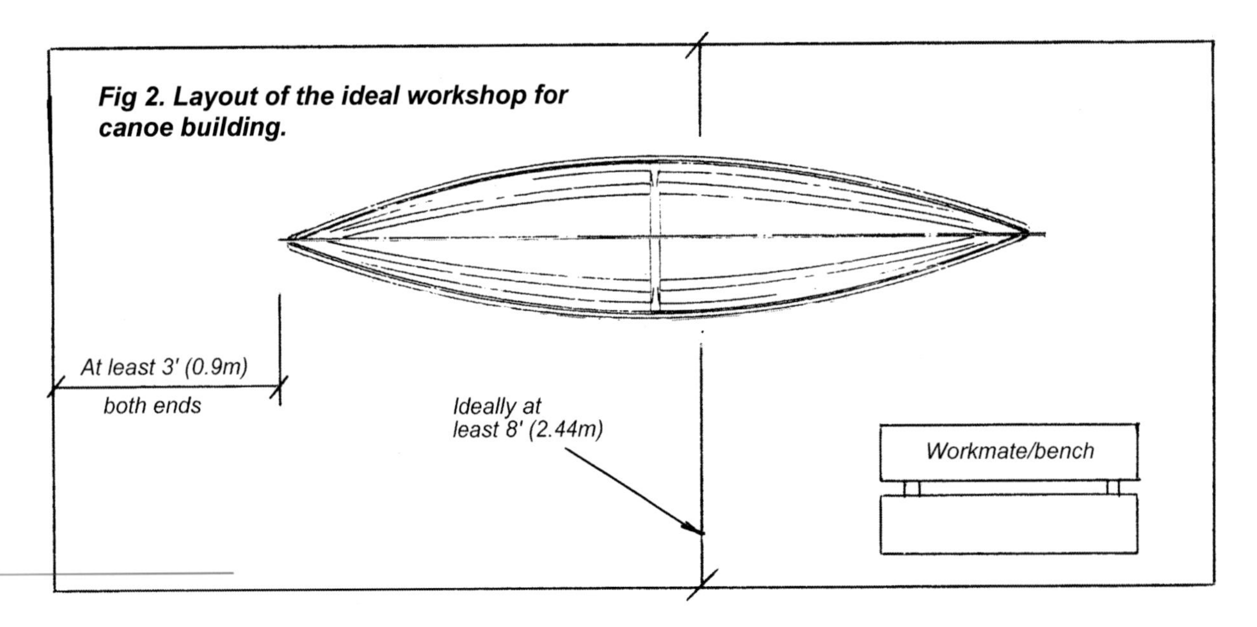

Fig 2. Layout of the ideal workshop for canoe building.

1.2 Tools

Let us talk about a minimum tool kit to start with. We are not using thick plywood or large sections of timber and much of what is required can come pre machined to the correct size from ordinary DIY stores and timber merchants, and therefore there is no need for a large or extensive tool kit.

My minimum kit includes :

For marking out:
A 4' (1.22m) straight edge (or a good straight piece of timber).
A 10' (3.05m) tape measure (or longer if possible).
Several good sharp pencils (I keep loosing them!).
A carpenter's square.
A plumb line (can be a large nut or bolt attached to a piece of string).
A carpenter's spirit level.

For cutting out and shaping:
A domestic single speed jig saw.
A small block plane.
An 18mm chisel.
A tenon saw (one of the cheap DIY variety will do).
A 10 oz. (or heavier if you prefer) hammer.
A nail punch.
A screw driver to fit 8G size screws.
An electric single speed drill or a hand drill with drill bits up to 1/4" (6mm) in dia.
An electric palm sander.
A Bradawl
At least 6 off 4'' (100mm) G clamps.
A Black & Decker type Workmate folding bench.

Consumable Items etc
These are items other than tools that you will need during the canoe construction.
Large/small yogurt type pots - for glue/resin mixing.
Mixing sticks - like large lollipop sticks.
Barrier cream - to protect your hands.
Acetone - for cleaning items coated in resin.
Masking tape - for holding some items together whilst gluing and for masking off areas that you do not want covered in glue/resin.
String/rope for use as tourniquets and Spanish windlasses to hold panels in place during the stitching process.

One or two notes about tools. As this is a short term project, borrow any tools that you do not have. You can get away with fewer tools than those already mentioned although most other books on canoe/boat building list many more tools as essential. For simple canoe construction, apart from the enjoyment of building your own boat, the idea, is to keep expense down. But, if there is a favourite tool not mentioned here, then use it (for instance, I like using a spoke shave).

Whilst you may not have many tools, do look after them and keep cutting edges sharp. It does make all the difference to the quality of the finished canoe.

1.3 Skills

The skills required depend on the standard of finish you want to achieve. I always say that basic DIY home skills are all that are required for stitch and tape construction. These are the ability to measure onto wood using sizes etc on the plans, basic cutting with hand tools and drilling plus the ability to use a jig-saw without injuring yourself!

But, if you want to show off exposed wood joints then you will need some further skills of the kind learnt in Wood-Working or Design Technology lessons at school—remember the teapot stand and garden dibber you made? These projects used the simple cross-halving joint and the mortice and tenon—the former is useful for stitch and tape construction but the latter is not really necessary – see Chapter 8 on Fitting-Out Canoes for more details on the type of halving joints used in canoe construction.

Below, a selection of basic power tools I use for canoe building

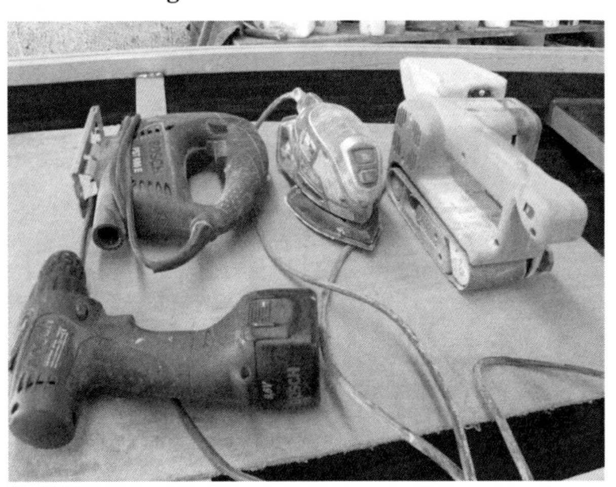

Above, a selection of typical hand tools used in plywood canoe construction.

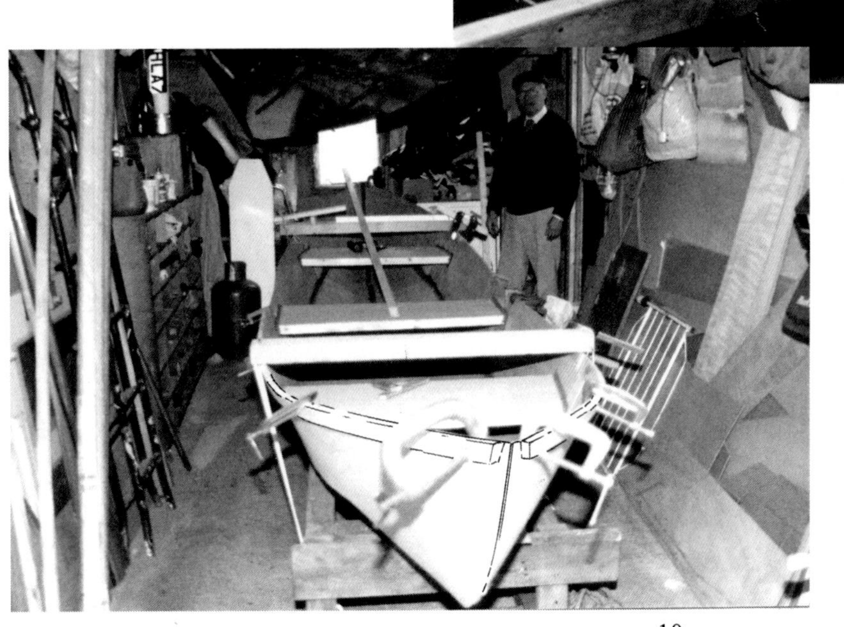

Above, the first Dart 16 kayak being built under a simple heavy duty PVC temporary shelter during a rather cold Spring and left, the first Beaver under construction in a very cluttered garage—both far from ideal but do-able!

Chapter 2

MATERIALS

FOR PLY CANOE CONSTRUCTION

2.1 Wood

2.1.1 Plywood

I have to say that I have met a lot of genuine Exterior grade WBP ply which is better than supposed Marine ply. True Marine ply will have veneers of equal thickness and of high quality (which usually means close grained). What often goes for Marine plywood, especially at 1/4'' (6mm) thickness, has a thick baulk core with very thin Gaboon outside veneers—Figure 3.

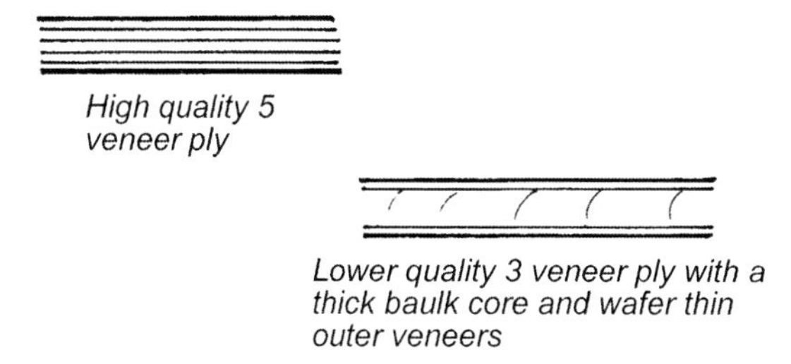

Fig 3. Plywood quality.

The Gaboon plywood usually originates from the Far East and can certainly be used. It can come apart, with the veneers separating, if it is bent or stressed too much but this is rare. I find that it is no better than much of the baulk core 3 veneer Exterior ply. A good quality Marine ply at a reasonable cost is BS1088 Meranti Marine ply which still has a thick core veneer, but which has stronger outside veneers made of a durable timber.

Aquaply and similar high quality plywoods are a multi-laminate ply and are Lloyds/RNLI approved. They are excellent, though less easy to bend than Meranti or Gaboon ply and is expensive.

I have often used exterior WBP ply for dinghies and canoes with great success but do be careful of weaknesses caused by voids in the Core veneer. European or Israeli exterior is the best. Far Eastern WBP tends to have all sorts of defects, but I have used it without failure.

You must simply watch out for voids and make sure that they are not put under stress. I have been asked about the suitability of Fir ply, especially since it is used in some countries for hull construction. The trouble is, it comes in so many grades, from the lowest grade shuttering ply to a grade which probably matches reasonable WBP Exterior. This is often coated with epoxies to make the ply last longer. My own opinion is, that with the cost of the epoxy, you may as well use Meranti Marine ply and feel safer about the quality of the hull surrounding you.

2.1.2 Timber (Softwood)

Because of the cost, I often use 1st quality White Pine (Deal) rather than Douglas Fir or Spruce, with as few knots as possible. It tends to go black when it gets wet for any length of time but is easily worked and is quite strong. Be careful about coating over screw holes etc as this is where the wood often goes black. If you want higher quality, Douglas Fir is a good compromise because it is relatively cheap and excellent for structural items. It is available in long lengths and is often used for solid spars. Western Red Cedar is an excellent lightweight wood. It is not as strong as Douglas Fir and it can also be expensive and is therefore only used for racing craft. Sitka Spruce has a good strength to weight ratio and is used for long items such as stringers, spars etc. Cost is high.

2.1.3 Timber (Hardwood)

I do not intend going into all the suitable hardwoods because it is the policy of Selway Fisher Design to keep the costs of constructing our boats down to a minimum and therefore to exclude expensive hardwoods wherever possible—in fact few of our canoe designs specify hardwoods at all. However, for those designs that do, or for those building to another designer's canoe designs which does specify hardwoods, here are a few notes about suitable hardwood types.

Keruing is cheap and durable but very hard to work (especially to plane) and is very heavy. It suffers from resinous voids. Iroko (sometimes known as African Teak) is an excellent wood which is cheap and has many of the properties and the durability of Burma Teak. It can warp after cutting and is therefore better used in thinner sections and laminated together and should be well fastened down. Afromosia is very durable and is easy to work with and is available in large sizes.

Brazilian Mahogany is an excellent material but is expensive. As an alternative Khaya is less durable but cheaper and usually easier to work. White Oak is very good and has less tendency to warp in thinner sizes but may need washing down with an agent to get rid of it's natural oil, before being glued.

2.2 Glues & Fastenings

DO NOT use PVA or any glue which does not say that it is definitely waterproof (water resistant is not good enough). This may sound obvious, but mistakes have been made! The cheapest marine glue in the larger quantities, was/is Cascamite (it also goes under the name Extramite), which is excellent for all general joiner work. However, it takes several hours to dry and is absolutely rigid and brittle and will therefore fracture if it is used to fill large gaps which are then stressed.

Aerolite 306 I have found to be excellent and comes in 2 parts. It dries clear and will take a certain amount of flexing and is therefore good for varnished woodwork. Cascamite dries to a cream colour. Aerodux is also very good but difficult to buy in small quantities and dries to a dark brown colour.

Another glue which has come onto the market is Balcotan 100 which has the advantage of being a one component glue. It is a polyurethane glue which cures on contact with moisture. It is used straight out of the container with no preparation or modification and comes in two types, regular and rapid. Regular cures in 4 to 8 hours and Rapid cures in 15 to 60 minutes depending upon the temperature. It seems to have fewer possible allergy problems than the epoxies because unlike the epoxies, it does not contain solvents and gives off little in the way of vapours.

On curing, it expands slightly and will readily fill gaps. However, it should not be used to fill gaps due to poor fitting joints - as far as I am aware, it is not designated as a gap filling glue (ie., a glue which will fill a gap and still be stronger than the surrounding wood). Because it expands on curing, the components of the joint should be well fastened together either by mechanical fastenings (screws and nails etc) or cramps to resist the glue pushing the components apart.

Balcotan 100 has other advantages, not least being the fact that it does not need 'thickening' with microfibres etc. It is already a glue, unlike the epoxies which are resins and which therefore need 'thickening/filling' before than can be used as glues. 'Filling' an epoxy resin means that it will go less far and partly because of this, you end up using less Balcotan 100 than you would epoxy.

Cleaning the joints up is also easier when using a polyurethane glue. With epoxy and most other glues, you must clean up the surrounding wood before any excess glue cures, trying to remove cured epoxy from around a joint often damages the wood. However, with Balcotan 100, you simply let any excess glue cure and then remove it with a cabinet scraper.

Most joints, if well glued, can be nailed rather than screwed, and I would recommend Gripfast barbed ring nails. Use the longest that the bury (total thickness of wood to be nailed) will allow. 12G are good for general use with 10G for heavy use. Brass boat nails can be used for low stress areas (ie., for nailing 1/4'' (6mm) ply seats onto supporting wood fillets). Because of their cost, I only use screws (brass or bronze) on joints which need to be pulled together.

2.3 Developments in Epoxies

The epoxies mentioned in Chapter 7 for work on stitch and tape joints are all of a general purpose type of which there are now several manufacturers and suppliers. Over the past few years some manufacturers have been developing new epoxies to suit particular applications. For instance, whilst the general purpose resins can be difficult to use when applying woven cloth because of their relatively high viscosity, some have developed lower viscosity resins for use with woven fabrics but which can also be filled to produce a filleting material. For instance Structural Polymers have their SP320 Spacote which has been developed as a lower viscosity resin for use with woven fabrics but which can also be filled to produce a filling material. Structural Polymers have also produced SPl10/210 specifically for woven fibre laminating and SP Spabond purely as a bonding adhesive—there are various derivatives for different applications including Spabond370 which is specifically for gluing Teak.

There is no doubt that these materials offer physical advantages over the simple use of a general purpose resin as a multi purpose material for gluing/bonding, filleting and the application of glass tape, but in using specialist materials you will inevitably end up spending more on ply canoe construction where you may finish with a whole load of half used products. It is very difficult to estimate the quantities of epoxies etc., required on a particular job as I have known some builders use half the epoxy on a particular boat, that somebody else uses on the same boat. However, for larger jobs and especially where you intend to coat an entire boat in epoxy, these new systems will provide an easier and better finished job.

2.4 Possible Problems with Epoxies

2.4.1 The Epoxy Will Not Cure

If the epoxy does not fully cure in the recommended time, there are several possible simple reasons. The first area to check, is that the correct mixing ratio has been used. In low temperatures, allow extra curing time and gently apply more localised heat (perhaps by building a temporary PVC shelter over the area being epoxied and using a low power heater).

Insufficient mixing can also be a problem, which is why I prefer to mix up small amounts of resin and hardener. The smaller amount being mixed, the easier it is to ensure a thorough mixing of resin and hardener.

Remember that it is essential to mix the resin and hardener together before adding any fillers and additives to the mix.

2.4.2 Failure in the Bond of Components being Glued Together

If we assume that the epoxy/filler mix has fully cured, then bond failure is most often due to a resin starved glue join. This can occur for two reasons. Either the porosity of the wood has caused the resin in the glue mix to 'soak' away from the joint or, too much clamping pressure has been applied and the epoxy mix has been squeezed out from the join.

If the wood is very porous or if you are gluing together end grain wood then 'prime' the wood first with unfilled resin/hardener. End grain should be 'primer' coated and the resin allowed to cure before further resin/ hardener is applied to finally glue the join together.

Also make sure that the surfaces to be bonded are not contaminated and that the bonding area is sufficiently large for the purpose of the joint.

2.4.3 Cloudy Appearance in Epoxy Coatings

Cloudy/white areas seen in the coating after the resin has cured are most often caused by moisture either from condensation or from very humid conditions. Coating early in the morning is usually a bad idea. Do any epoxy coating mid day or in the afternoon. If you have sanded down the previous resin coat using wet and dry sand paper do make sure that there is no moisture left on the surface before applying the next epoxy coat.

The only way to get rid of this cloudiness, is to cut the resin coats back by sanding down and then wash the surface down to remove the amine blush. Make sure that all surfaces are thoroughly dry and then re-coat.

Cloudiness can also be caused by over vigorous brushing or rolling on of the epoxy coat. This traps air in the resin which does not escape and again this will have to be cut back to remove the cloudiness. You should also use a special coating resin or one which uses a different hardner to make the epoxy less viscous (WEST 207 special coating hardener for instance). As with painting and varnishing, always apply resin coats in thin layers.

2.4.4 Runs in the Epoxy Coating

This is caused by too thick a coat of resin being applied or perhaps the resin taking too long to cure. So, the cure is either to warm the resin before applying it, or too use a faster hardener. Overall, I have found that simply putting the resin container into a bowl of hot water to raise it's temperature is the best solution. Not only does this raise the temperature of the resin so that it cures quicker after application but it also lowers the viscosity of the resin so that it is easier to apply. In fact, when I am using the epoxy to wet out glass tape for stitch and tape seams, I always pre-heat the resin container in warm water and I find that the resin wets out the glass tape easier allowing you to use less resin. This is an important tip when taping in cool temperatures. I have been able to halve the amount of resin used by pre-heating as against trying to use it in it's cold state.

2.4.5 Other Coating Products will not Cure over Epoxy

In this case, the epoxy may not have fully cured. I always leave epoxy coatings three to four days or more in temperatures of at least 60 degrees before over coating with paint or varnish.

There may also be a problem with compatibility between the hardener used in the epoxy and the coating being used. Single part polyurethanes may not cure over epoxy. In the main. I have found little trouble with most conventional oil based paints (for instance many exterior household paints) but they do sometimes take more time to cure. If possible, do a test piece before committing yourself to a particular paint or varnish system.

Preparation of the epoxy surface before applying the paint or varnish is essential. Make sure that any amine blush is removed and that the surface is well sanded before applying the coating—see 2.4.3.

If a paint or varnish is not curing after it has been applied over an epoxy coated surface, I leave it to dry as far as possible over a day or two and then wash it down with white spirit. I then allow this to dry and coat with another thin coat of paint or varnish—usually this works.

2.4.6 Typical Material Requirements for an Average 16' (4.9m) Canoe

Wood

Plywood
4 sheets of 4,5 or 6mm (I always tend to use exterior WBP grade for canoes).

Deal (White Pine)
33' of 5/8" x 5/8" (10m of 15x15mm)
33' of 5/8" x 1 1/2" (10m of 15x35mm)
26' of 3/4" x 3/4" (8m of 18x18mm)
18' of 1" x 2" (5.5m of 25x50mm)

Go for wood sizes that you can get 'off the shelf' if necessary, under the above sizes.

Glues & Epoxies

0.75kg of Balcotan Adhesive.

2kg of Epoxy (i.e. WEST 105/205).
50m of 50mm glass woven roving tape (ie. WEST Episize glass tape).
5m of 75mm glass woven roving tape.
The smallest quantity you can get of epoxy filler poweder (ie. WEST 407 low density).

Fastenings

I use approximately 50 or 60 off 3/4" x 8G (18mm x 8G) brass screws and about 30 off 1 1/4" x 8G (30mm x 8G) brass screws.

Paints & Varnishes

Approximately 1-2 litres of marine Gloss Varnish.
2 litres of undercoat paint and 1 litre of gloss paint (both exterior household grade).

Larger Canoes from the Selway Fisher stable

17' Prospector

20' Freight

35' Dragon

18' Waka Ama

Chapter 3

PRODUCING THE HULL PLANKS

3.1 Marking Out the Planks

The first stage of building a stitch and tape boat is to mark and cut out the plywood planks. Plank shapes are rarely successful when given full-size unless they are plotted onto expensive Mylar sheets – plotting onto ordinary paper is not very accurate as the paper will shrink and stretch and for larger boats with long panels/planks, this can be disastrous. Over the years I have had several clients talk to me about the problems that they have encountered using full-size templates mainly due to slight variations in the plotting scale which should of course be full-size (1:1) but is not always so and a small discrepancy can be disastrous over an 8' (2.44m) length of plank.

On Selway Fisher Design plans we use a simple method of accurately marking out the plank/panel shapes directly onto the plywood sheets. It does involve the use of a tape measure and transferring measurements given on the drawings onto the sheets of plywood, but it is accurate. Alternatively, you can go to one of the growing firms who can take our DXF files and use them to router or laser cut the panels for you (www.jordanboats.co.uk for instance). To mark out the planks/panels yourself, follow this simple method :-

A. Look at the design sheet showing the hull panel/plank shapes and you will see a drawing showing one or more standard sheets of plywood laid edge to edge with the panel/plank shapes drawn on them and a series of parallel station lines drawn across the ply. These are usually spaced at 305mm (12") intervals. The dimensions for the panel/plank shapes are measured along these station lines – so the first job is to draw these station lines down onto the plywood – see Figure 4.

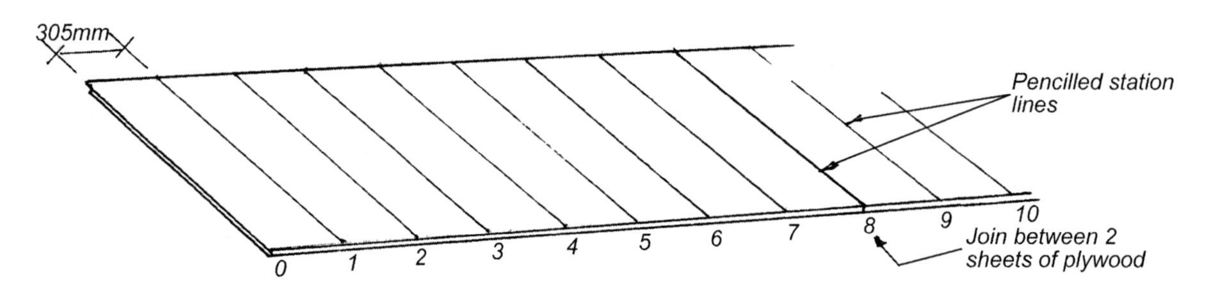

Fig 4.

B. Next, put your tape measure along each of these station lines in turn and mark off the dimensions given for the top and bottom (chine, gunwale lines etc) of each panel – Figure 5. Take your time and make sure you make a bold mark for each measurement – note that in most cases all the dimensions given are measured from the lower edge of the ply sheet.

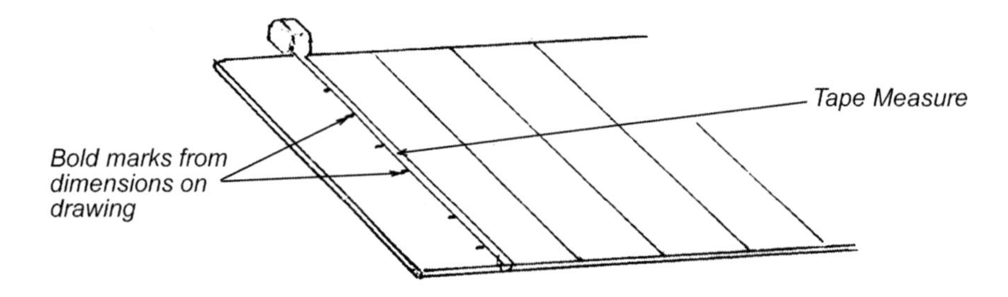

Fig 5.

C. You can now mark the end points for each line – for instance, at the bow end of each panel the end points are defined by a distance up from the lower edge of the plywood sheet and horizontally from an adjacent station line – see Figure 6.

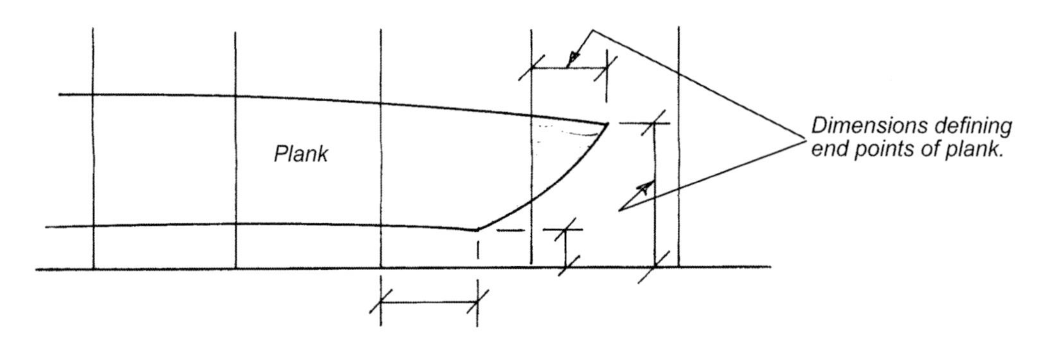

Fig 6.

D. Sometimes a particular curve (often a bow end curve), is defined by a series of squares – see Figure 7 – the size of the squares will be given – draw these onto the plywood sheet aligned as shown against a station line, and sketch in the curve using the squares as a guide.

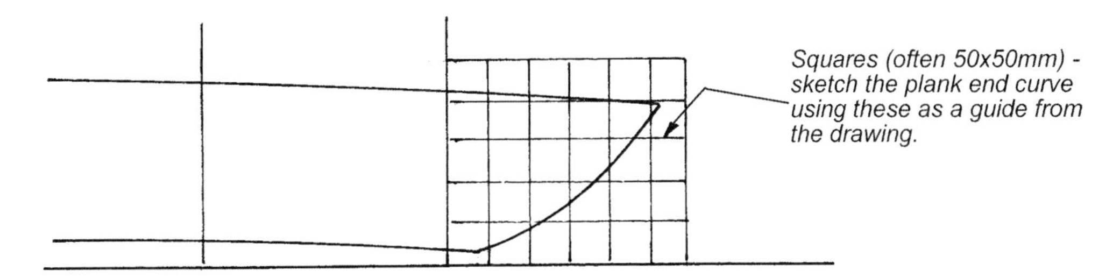

Fig 7.

E. Now we can draw in the long curves defining the panels/planks – do this using a long thin batten (a piece of old plastic curtain rail or thin plastic wiring conduit which you can obtain from a DIY store, is excellent for this) – hold the batten down with weights or nails to pass through each mark on the station lines and draw in each curve with a bold pencil line – see Figure 8.

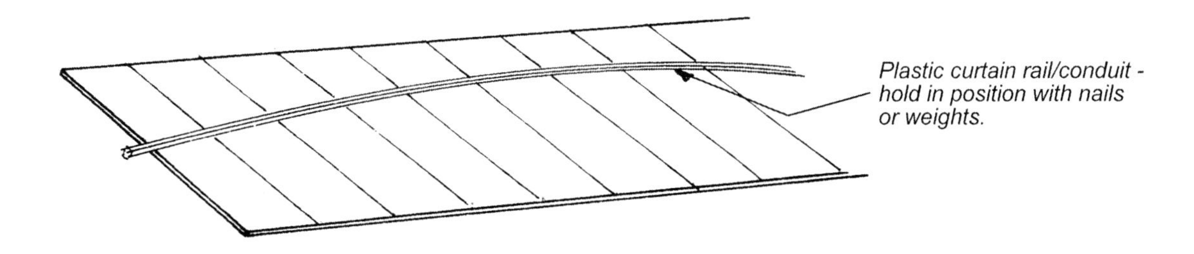

Fig 8.

F. Mark any frame positions given on the drawings onto the hull panels/planks.

3.2 Cutting Out the Hull Planks

Now you can cut out the panel/plank shapes – I use a single speed jig saw with a fine blade holding the ply sheet on a workmate/saw horse – cut approximately 1mm from the line. You can either mark out each panel separately (port and starboard) or mark and cut out one set of panels (say the port side) and use these as templates for the other set (starboard side).

Some builders have successfully cramped (or bolted) 2 sheets of plywood together, one on top of the other and then used a jig-saw to cut the planks out of both sheets at one time. This means that there is only a need to mark out one set of planks. If you do this, use a new high quality jig-saw blade and make sure that the jig-saw foot is set accurately at 90 degrees to the blade and that the blade does not bend during the cutting so that the bottom plywood plank ends up smaller than the top plywood plank.

I have also hand cut planks using a Tenon saw held at a shallow angle, especially if there are no tight curves on the plank shapes. This takes a lot of effort but allows you to cut closer to the line and low grade plywood is less likely to shatter using a hand saw.

Once all the planks/panels have been cut out, you can use your workmate (bench vice etc) to hold each individual pair of planks/panels together so that they can be planed up carefully to the line. In a canoe symmetrical about the centre or mid point you will be planing up four pieces of ply plank/panel together.

Match each pair of planks together and clamp each end.

Use a couple of workmates to hold the planks vertically and use a plane to trim them down to the line.

A square is used to make sure that you are planning/trimming the edges all the same and not taking too much off one side or the other.

Chapter 4

JOINING LONG PLANKS TOGETHER

4.1 General

For any boat over 7'9" long, the plank lengths will need to be joined at some point when using standard 8' (2.44m) sheets of plywood. There are 2 basic/common methods of joining ply planks together which are longer than the standard 8' (2440 mm) sheets of ply. These are the Butt Strap and Scarf methods.

The Butt strap is the simplest method and is strong but does leave a rather ugly block on the inside of the hull and can give you a hard spot on the hull. The Scarf joint is strong (if it is done correctly) and is far neater and almost gives you a plank that looks continuous without any hard spots, but it requires a long bench to work on and some careful use of the plane.

4.1.1 Butt Straps

For thin ply up to 4mm in thickness and for lightweight boats such as canoes, you can butt the ply together and simply tape the butt join both sides of the plank, with 3'' (75mm) woven roving tape. This is the method employed on the Dart, Waterman and Wren canoes and is quick and simple (Figure 9). Apply the tape in the same way as mentioned in Chapter 8 priming the ply first with the resin. I have successfully used this method with polyester type 'A' resin but epoxy would of course, be stronger. Make sure that

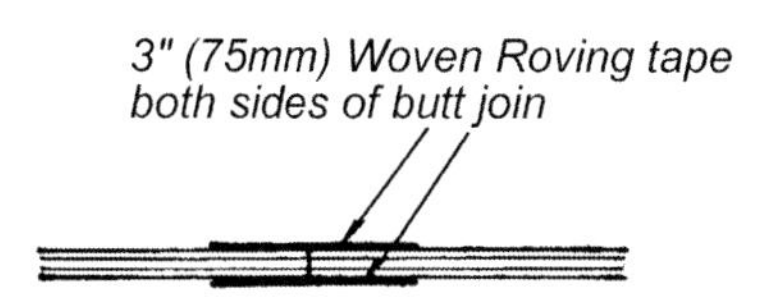

Fig 9. A simple glass tape butt join.

Above—two parts of a plank butted together over softwood which has been covered in PVC and temporarily nailed in place (outside the glass butt strap area. The plywood has been given a coat of the epoxy resin/hardener mix ready for the tape to be applied.

Above—the glass tape has been applied and has thoroughly wetted out. This is now left to cure , the nails removed and the plank is carefully turned over ready to have a second glass tape applied on the other face of the plank.

the ply planks are held down onto a flat surface. It is better to do this with weights set either side of the join—or nail each piece down to a piece of softwood.

Boats made from 5 or 6mm ply and above, require ply butt straps. These are applied to the inboard side of the planks only and are of equal thickness to the ply plank. If the butt strap is not wide enough, then you will end up with a hard spot where the ply plank moves away from lying in a flush line with it's mating part (Figure 10). On the other hand, if the strap is too wide, it will prevent the plank from bending around any curve that you have to induce into it when fitting it to the hull.

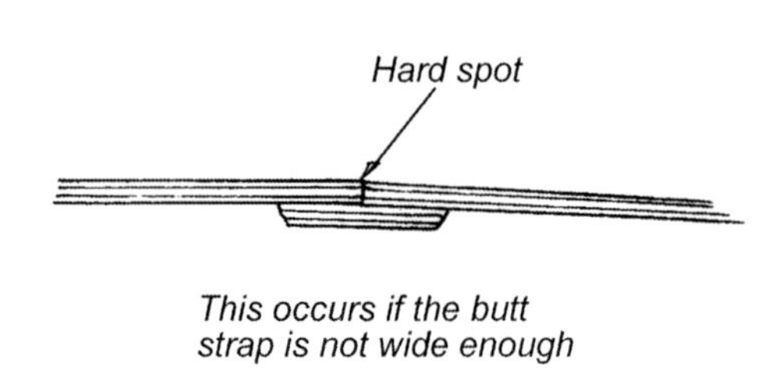

Fig 10. A hard spot on the butt join.

I have found that 4'' to 5'' (100-125mm) wide butt straps are ideal for boats made from 1/4'' (6mm) ply and 6'' (150mm) for 3/8'' (9mm) ply and 8'' (200mm) for 1/2'' (12mm) ply. The ply pieces of plank should be butt joined on a hard flat surface covered with pvc (to prevent any excess glue from attaching the ply to the work surface) and plenty of glue should be used during the process applying it to the mating edges of the pieces of ply plank first (Figure 11).

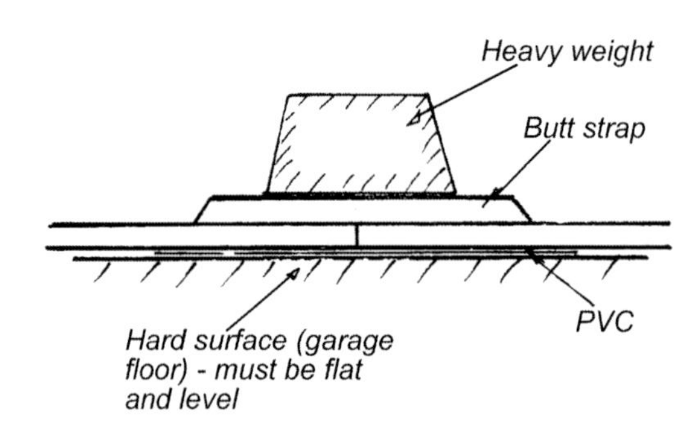

Fig 11. Applying a ply butt strap.

For piece of mind, I like to fasten the butt strap into place with boat nails. I do this by

assembling one of the pieces of ply plank to the strap with the strap underneath and hammering the nails through from the outside so that they pass into a scrap piece of wood held under the strap (Figure 12). Apply more glue and fit the other piece of plank, and nail it in the same way. Carefully turn the plank over (you will need some help) and with a chisel remove the scrap pieces of wood exposing the ends of the nails. Having made sure that the planks are lying flat, you can then hammer the ends of the nails over to lie across the grain of the ply.

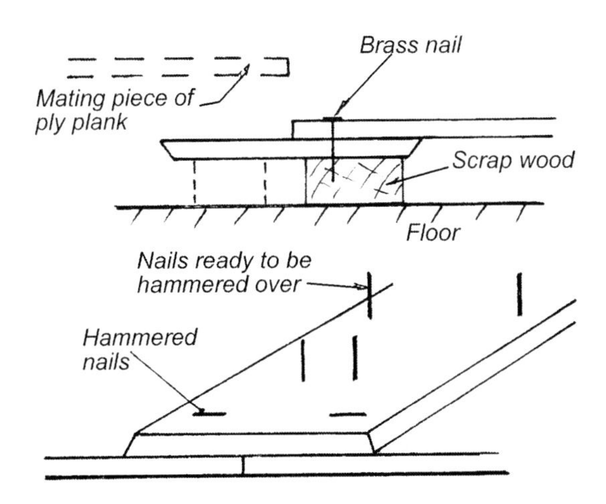

Fig 12. Nailing a butt strap—alternatively, use small screws.

If the plans you are working from do not specify the position of the butt straps in the planks then position them away from frames and bulkheads and in such a manner, that straps on adjacent planks are not near each other. Also, take into account the inside WR tape on stitch and tape boats and cut the strap short to keep it clear of the edge of the ply so that the tape does not have to run over the strap.

For 3/8'' (9mm) ply and above, use screws instead of nails to fasten the straps. Both nails and screws should be put in staggered and at 3'' (75mm) spacing (Figure 13).

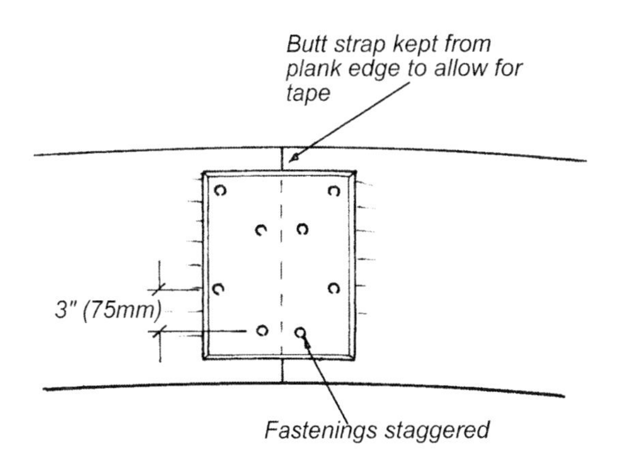

Fig 13. Larger butt straps.

Above—a typical plywood butt strap.

4.1.2 Scarf Joining Planks

The length of a scarf joint should be 6 to 8 times the thickness of the plank, so that for a 1/4'' (6mm) plank, it should be around 2'' (50mm) long (Figure 14). Because you are not simply butting the planks together scarfing the planks will mean that you will have to allow for the length of the scarf when marking and cutting out the plank pieces. The best way to do this, is to mark out one part of the plank as normal, but then to start marking the mating piece of plank the length of the scarf joint away from the edge of the ply sheet. The lines for the edge of the plank should be projected back over the scarf allowance (Figure 15).

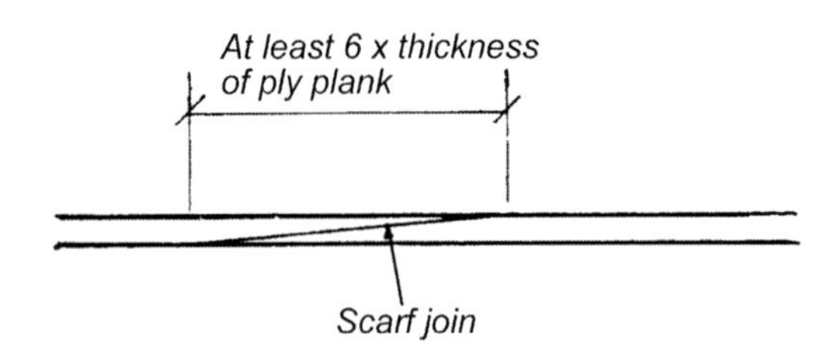

Fig 14. An edge-on view of a scarf join.

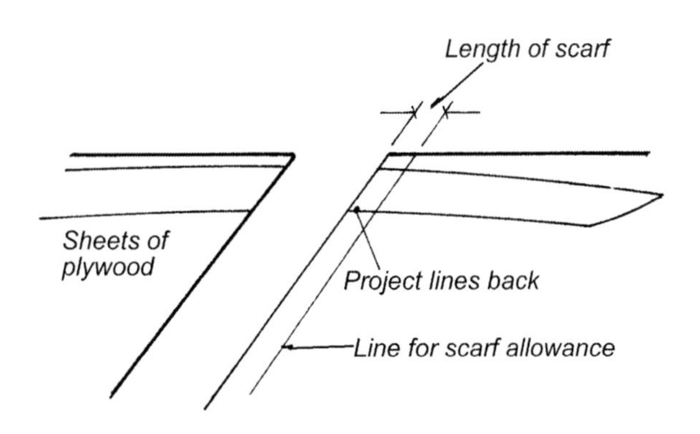

Fig 15. Marking out the planks with the additional width required for the scarf.

The best way to plane scarfs, is to do 2 or more at a time by clamping them to a bench top with the edge of the lower plank up to the edge of the bench and the next plank on top of the first, but with it's edge butting up to the inner scarf line of the lower plank (Figure 16). Plane carefully with a sharp, finely set plane, using the plywood laminates as a guide. These will show as straight lines across the ply, if the surface that you are planing is flat. Check that the surface is good and flat with a straight edge.

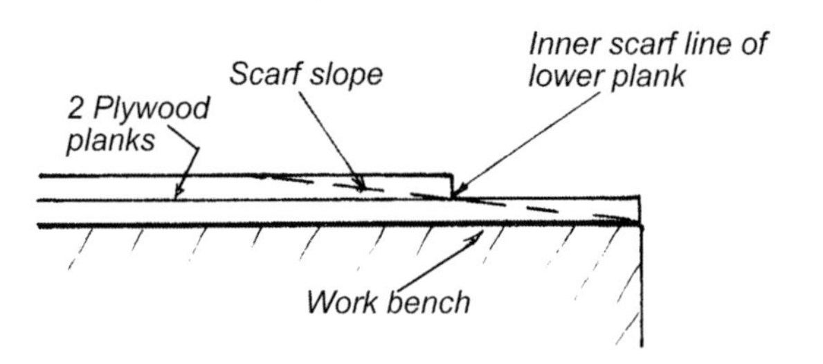

Fig 16. Setting up the planks.

Above—planning a scarf on two planks at once and using the plywood laminates as a guide.

When gluing the scarf joint, put PVC down first, apply the glue liberally and use heavy staples to hold the ply together and to prevent it from slipping whilst you clamp it up. This is a slightly delicate operation and it is best to have some patient help around. The cramps should be applied over lengths of wood above and below the joint so that the clamping pressure is spread evenly across the width of the joint. Use PVC (plastic shopping bags) between the lengths of wood and the plank to prevent them from sticking to the plank.

Above—clamping a scarf join.

Once the glue has cured, the cramps can be removed and the edges of the plank planed up. For scarfed planks especially, you may need to check that the planks have been correctly aligned (do this before the glue has cured!) by running a line between the lower fore and aft points of the plank and checking the measurement from the line to the middle lower edge of the plank against the drawings—you can also use a line drawn on each plank half as an alternative—Figure 17).

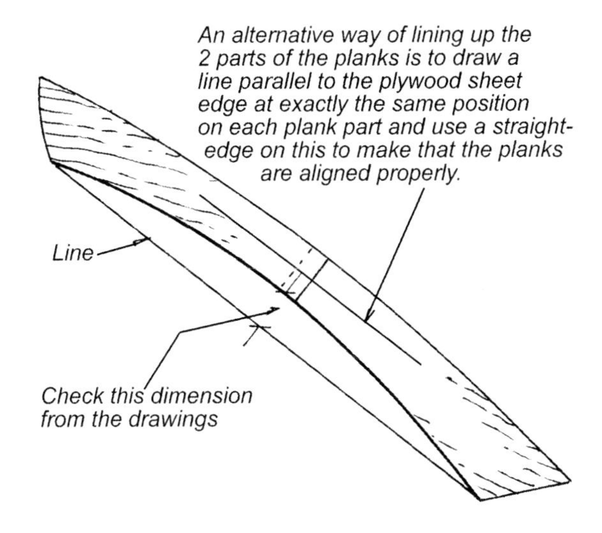

Fig 17. Checking the overall shape of the plank.

4.1.3 Saw Tooth or Castellated Join

This is a rare but quite a neat and simple method of joining plank lengths together. Basically, a truncated saw tooth shape is cut into the end of one plank piece and it's matching shape is cut into the end of the other plank.

Figure 18 gives typical dimensions for a 4 to 6mm ply plank. This method is really appropriate for fairly narrow planks.

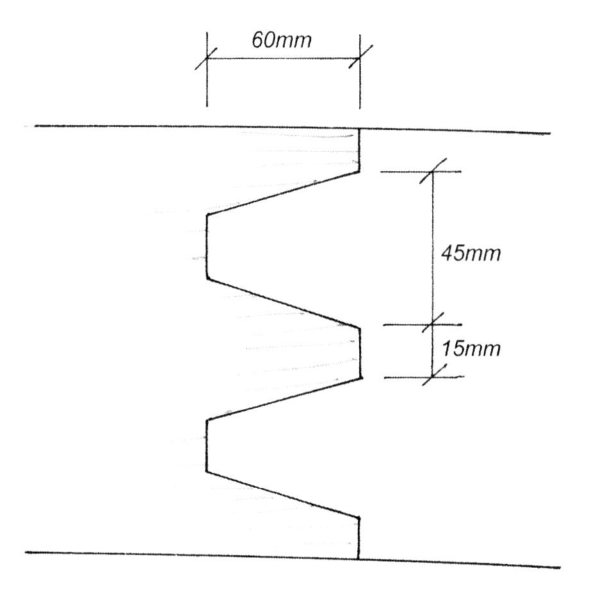

Fig 18. The shape of the saw tooth/castellated join in 6mm plywood.

First, carefully mark out the shape of the castellation onto the end of one plank/panel. Cut this out using a tenon saw to cut the lines that go along the plank (at an angle) and cut along the lines across the plank with a coping saw (I prefer to fully imprint these latter lines by using a chisel and mallet on them).

When marking out the plank shape onto the mating piece of ply, you must allow for the length of the join (in much the same way as you do for a scarf join) by adding this measurement onto the end of the plank. At this point, the plank piece which has already been cut out should be placed over the unmarked end of the second plank piece. Line up the two plank pieces very carefully, making sure that both pieces are positioned to give the correct plank curve and then clamp them together to prevent any movement.

Take a sharp pencil and using the plank already cut as a template, mark the shape onto the second piece of planking. This may then be carefully cut out.

Because the glue will be applied to end grain plywood, the end of the ply should be pre-coated with epoxy resin (allowing this to cure). Further thickened epoxy can then be applied and the two pieces of plank brought together. Lay the gluing pieces together onto a flat surface which has been covered with PVC and hold down with weights.

This is also a good method to use, if you intend joining oversize pieces of ply together before marking and cutting out the plank shapes.

Above—a saw tooth/castellated join .

Below—on many plywood canoes the join between the 2 parts of each plank length will occur at one place, usually in the centre of the canoe, as can be seen on this Christine design here—there is no structural problem with this for small boats and canoes.

Chapter 5

STITCHING THE PLANKS TOGETHER

5.1 Preparing the Planks for Stitching

The planks now need to be stitched together along what are called the 'chine' seams—a 'chine' is simply the 'corner' between two planks on a plywood boat. So, the first job is to drill as many of the holes as you can to take the stitches. Precise measurement for the holes is not required as most of the stitches will be removed later and their spacing will not usually show up on the finished canoe. The stitches may be copper wire (1/16'' in dia (1.5mm), for most canoes to 1/8'' dia (3mm) for large canoes over 18' (5.5m) in length. I obtain the copper wire from scrap electrical cabling but I also use iron binding wire (very cheap), gardening wire (nylon coated) and bailing wire. The main requirement is that it is strong enough to hold the joint together and ductile enough to be easily twisted together to form the tie.

Cable ties may also be used but I still prefer to use wire as once tightened, you cannot release cable ties and they can be expensive.

For 1/8" to 1/4" (3-6mm) ply, keep your drill holes about 1/4" (6mm) from the edge of the ply and unless the area is highly stressed the spacing between the ties can be between 8 and 12 inches (200-300mm) - Figure 19. Put in more ties where the shape requires it.

You cannot drill all the holes required as it is difficult to match holes in adjacent planks before you start to stitch. The rule is, at each chine seam, drill the holes in one plank only and then drill it's matching hole in the adjacent plank as you start to stitch the planks

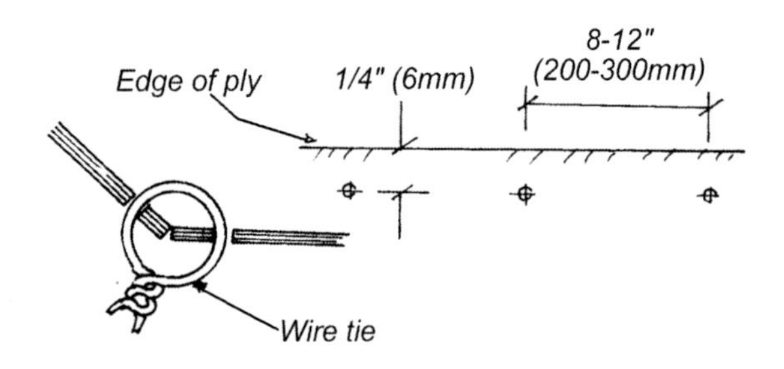

Fig 19. Drilling the holes for the stitches.

together and bend them into place. The only seam where this does not apply is the centreline seam on the first set of planks.

So, starting with the bottom pair of planks, lay them on a bench, match them up and drill the holes through both planks for the centreline seam. At the same time, drill the holes along the top of the planks for the first chine seam. Put this first pair of plank to one side and then repeat the process on the top edge of the remaining planks with the exception of the top most plank which you do not drill at all for the moment.

Above—drilling the first set of holes—do this over a bench or, if not convenient, hold a wood block under the planks as you drill so that the veneer on the underside plank does not break out as you drill through—be careful not to drill your hand!

5.2 Stitching the Planks

I am often asked whether to stitch any plywood frames/bulkheads in place at the same time as you stitch the planks together. It depends on the design and how stiff and awkward the planks are to get into place. I often find it a good idea to start stitching the frames/bulkheads into place after the first 2 or 3 planks have been loosely stitched together. You do not want everything to be too rigid at an early stage as there is often some adjustment, perhaps with a plane, to be made, especially towards the bows.

Lay the first pair of planks together and loosely stitch through the centre line seam but do not go too far up the curve of the bow. Now, whilst supporting the planks on a couple of work benches or saw horses, open them out—do not worry about getting the planks into their correct position at this stage.

Start stitching the next pair of planks in place using a reference point to start from—in a canoe this may be the centre seam where the plank lengths are joined together. Keep the stitches loose so that adjustments fore and aft can be made later.

Just how far you start to pull the bow together at this stage, is a matter for careful consideration. Some samples of plywood are definitely much more stiff than others of the same thickness and manufacture. I also find that it is sometimes best to leave the bow entirely until I have all the planks stitched together—adjacent planks often help each other in forming the correct shape at the bow.

When you are stitching the bow together, if there is a lot of stress in bending some of the planks into place, you can use string ties with a simple Spanish Windlass to help. Whilst the ties are being secured, the ply can also be forced together with sash clamps (Figure 20). The string ties are passed through holes in the ply which will eventually be filled after the string has been removed. When the next panel of ply is stitched into place, the string can be accommodated in a small groove filed into the bottom edge of the next panel. It is unusual to find the planks difficult to bend in shape unless you are using 1/4" (6mm) ply on a canoe with only one chine.

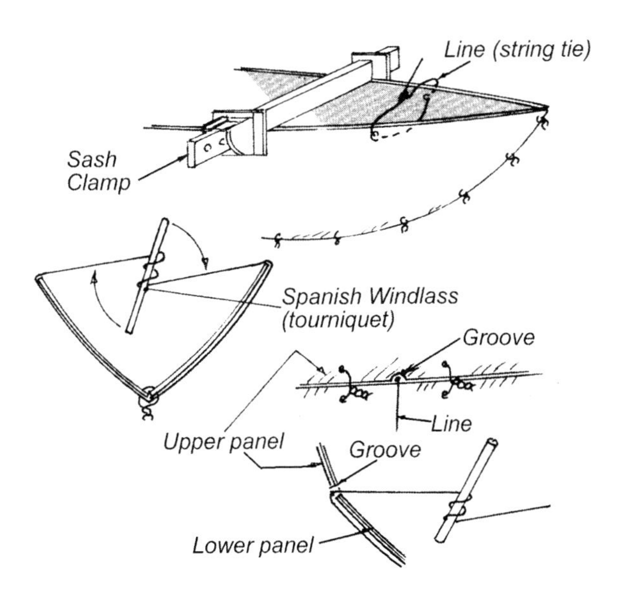

Fig 20. Using clamps and tourniquets to help force the planks into position.

I repeat, whilst stitching the hull together, do not twist the wire too tight in case any adjustments need to be made. If there are any tight spots, release the wire and carefully trim the edges of the ply with a block plane (Figure 21).

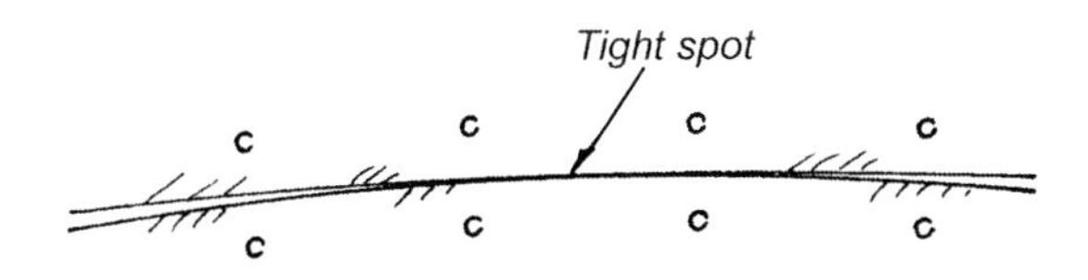

Fig 21. A 'tight' area along the chine seam.

If the ply is difficult to force into shape, you can also steam it by wrapping the ply above and below in towels and pour boiling water over it. The towels will retain the water and heat and help the outer veneers (where there will be most tension and compression) to stretch and contract more easily (Figure 22). Initially soak the outside of the bend only as this may be all that is required, but if this does not succeed, soak both sides.

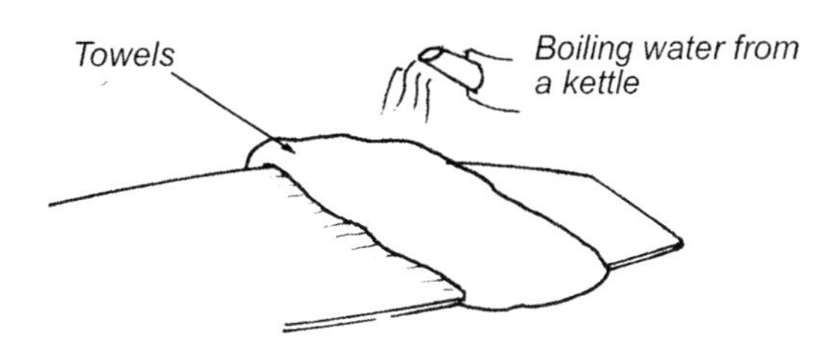

Fig 22. Using hot water to 'steam' a ply panel and make it more supple.

Plywood of the same thickness and specification but from different manufacturers will bend by different amounts. Good quality Marine ply with thin veneers (ie. 5 veneers in 1/4'' (6mm) ply) is much stiffer than lower quality 3 veneer ply with it's wafer thin outer veneers (Figure 3).

5.3 Stitching the Transom in Place (Outboard Motor Canoes)

You can leave stitching the transom in place until all the planks have been stitched or do it as you go. I tend to put it in after I have the first 2 or 3 pairs of planks together. The transom usually sits inside the planks so you want to drill a hole towards the top and bottom of each plank just ahead of the transom. Drill matching holes in the transom starting from the bottom and stitching up before you drill the next hole.

5.4 Final Tightening of the Stitches

Once all the planks are in place along with any transom and frames/bulkheads there may be, you can start to tighten all the stitches. Start at the centreline seam and work your way up each plank in turn—start from the middle and work towards the ends. As you do so, push the planks so that the inner corners of the plank edges meet together and do not overlap.

Where two planks seem too tight together with gaps either side of the tight spot, release the wires so that you can use a small block plane to take of some material.

Gaps up to 3 or 4mm are no problem—anything more will need filling with a sliver of wood epoxied in place. Smaller gaps are dealt with by fixing a piece of masking tape to the outside of the seam and applying thickened epoxy to the gap on the inside of the chine seam. This is done when we start to prepare the seams for taping but not now because we have got to check the shape of the canoe before going any further.

Below and the next three pages show a Hazelnut canoe being stitched together

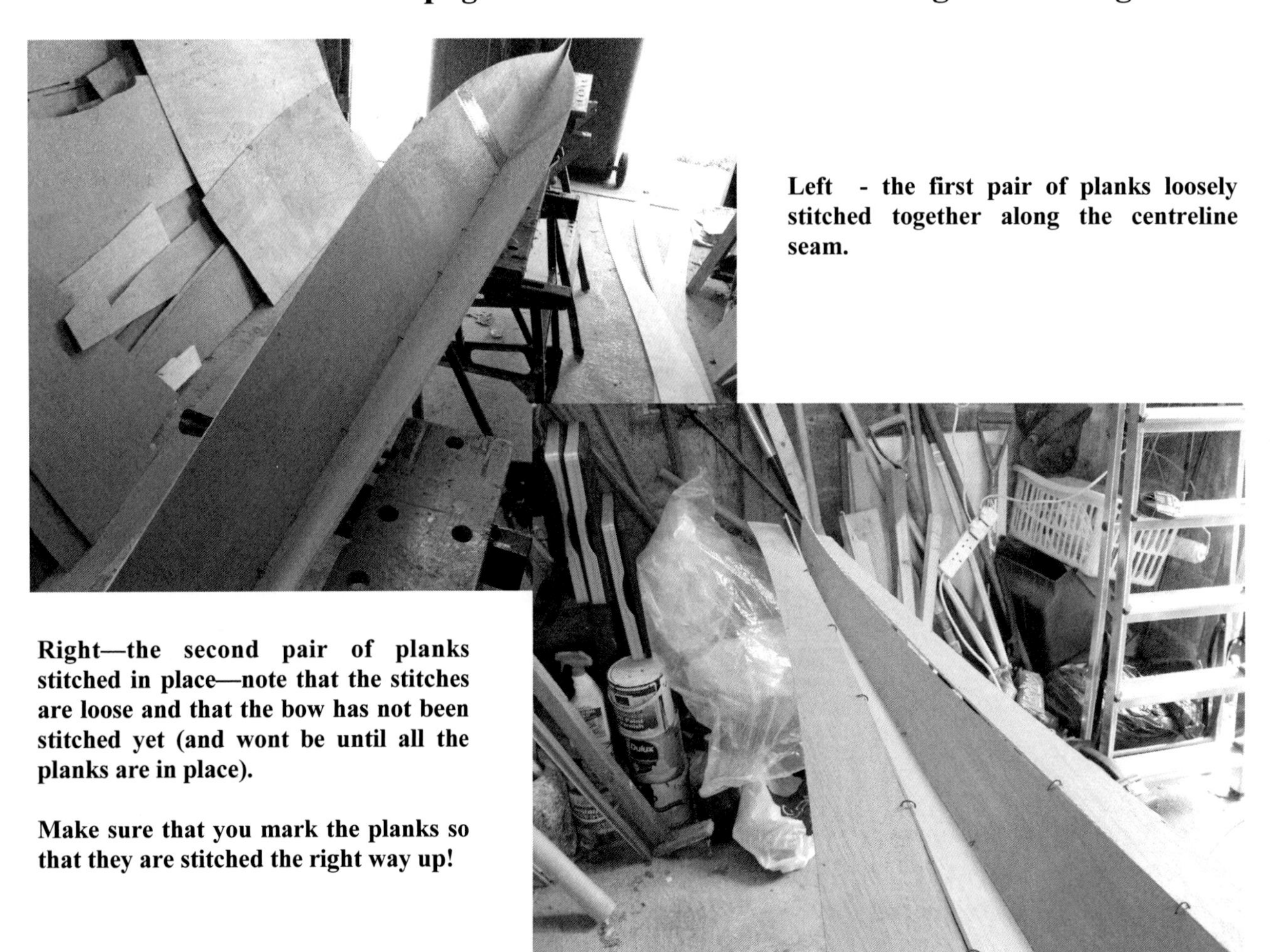

Left - the first pair of planks loosely stitched together along the centreline seam.

Right—the second pair of planks stitched in place—note that the stitches are loose and that the bow has not been stitched yet (and wont be until all the planks are in place).

Make sure that you mark the planks so that they are stitched the right way up!

Left—3 planks attached and looking nothing like a canoe at this stage until, below, the bulkheads are stitched into place.

Right and below —when stitching the ply frames/bulkheads in place the stitch goes through the plank either side of the bulkhead. The positions for the bulkheads have been marked onto the planks from dimensions given on the drawings.

Right—stitching the frames/bulkheads into place starts to pull the planks into their correct position.

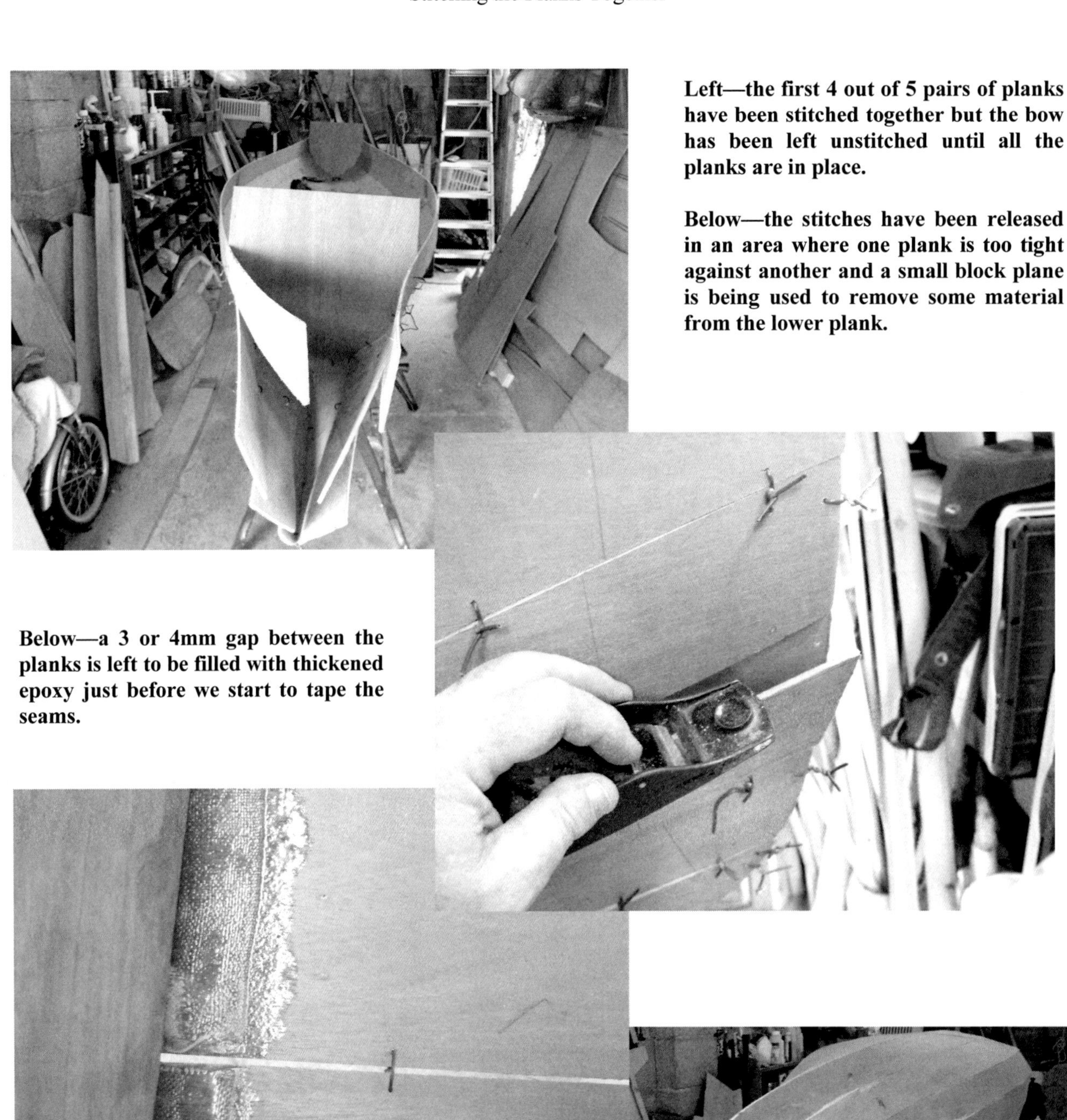

Left—the first 4 out of 5 pairs of planks have been stitched together but the bow has been left unstitched until all the planks are in place.

Below—the stitches have been released in an area where one plank is too tight against another and a small block plane is being used to remove some material from the lower plank.

Below—a 3 or 4mm gap between the planks is left to be filled with thickened epoxy just before we start to tape the seams.

Once you stitch the bow together, it is essential to unstitch where necessary and use a block plane to shape a smooth curve on the bow—this has already been done and the seams re-stitched and the inside seams taped resulting in an attractive bow curve awaiting it's exterior tape—right.

Chapter 6

CHECKING THE SHAPE OF THE CANOE

6.1 Checking the Shape of the Canoe

After you have stitched all the seams together but before the seams have been taped or epoxied, you must check the canoe to ensure that it is square and not twisted or out of shape. You must also ensure that bulkheads/frames and any seats already cut, fit correctly and are not causing any hard spots in the hull skin.

If the hull is twisted, then some bracing will be required to force it into shape whilst the seams are finished. An easy way to check whether there is a twist in the hull, is to sight along the tops of frames/bulkheads and any transom to see whether all the top lines of these components are parallel to each other (Figure 23).

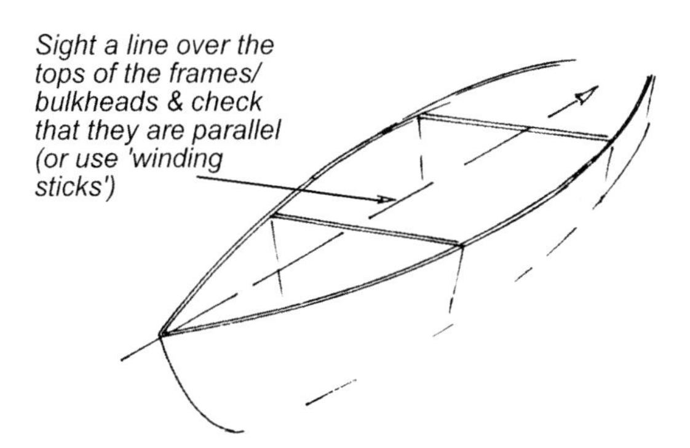

Fig 23. Checking over the tops of the frames to make sure the hull is untwisted.

Above—2 or 3 lengths of wood batten are used as 'winding sticks' by laying them across the gunwales to check for twist in the hull—if the sticks appear parallel there is no twist.

Measurements can be taken from the stem to the ends of each frame/bulkhead where they meet the hull sides to see whether they are the same both sides and a plumb line can be used to check whether the frames etc., are vertical (Figure 24). Because you have no definite building jig, there is no accurate reference points to work to, but you can get most components sitting in a level or vertical position by eye and the judicious use of a hammer. You can finally tighten up the wire ties as you do this.

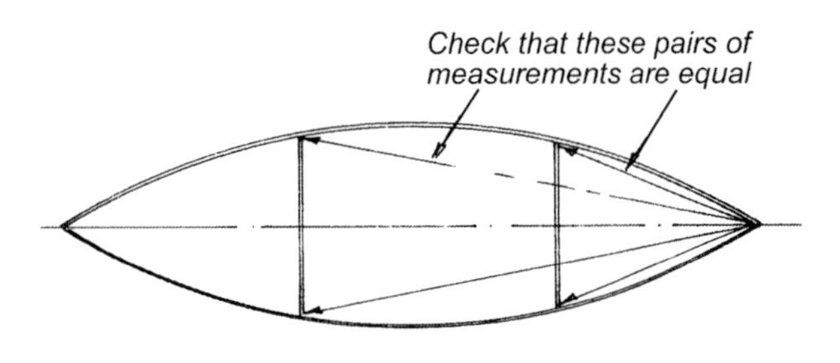

Fig 24. Using pairs of dimensions to check the shape.

6.2 Correcting the Shape of the Canoe

Use scrap timber to brace out gunwales or to force a panel up or down, or in or out by jamming one end against a wall, ceiling or floor with the other end on a hull panel (Figure 25). This latter end should have a ply pad under it to prevent bruising the wood. Heavy weights can also be used to good effect.

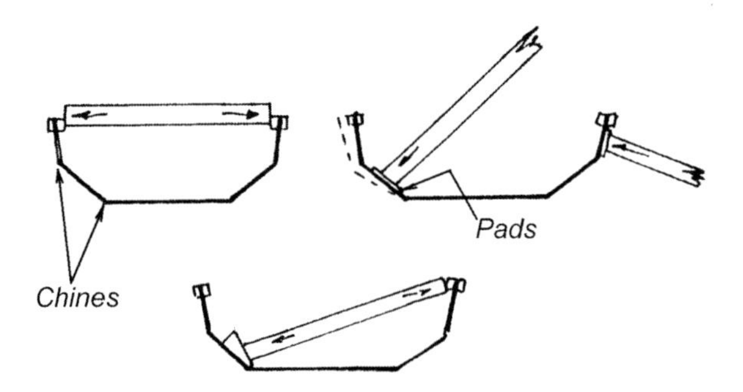

Fig 25. Pushing the boat into shape.

Remember that towels spread over a stiff area and soaked in boiling water from a kettle will also help, but do not soak the wood too much as it will raise the wood fibres and could weaken the area under stress, especially if you are using low grade baulk cored plywood. You must also let the wood dry thoroughly whilst it is being held in shape by struts, cramps etc., before using wood glue or resin in the area.

Chapter 7

STITCH AND TAPE SEAMS

& EPOXY FILLETING FRAMES ETC IN PLACE

7.1 General

Having stitched all the seams and checked that the hull is untwisted and the correct shape, we can now think about completing the chine seams to make them structurally sound and waterproof and also, permanently fix any plywood frames and bulkheads into place. Looking at the chine seams first, the process is done, usually both on the inboard and outboard sides of the seams by applying a glass woven roving (WR) tape and soaking it in a resin. The resin 'wets out', that is, soaks through the tape and cures to form a glass/resin matrix which adheres firmly to the plywood and forms a waterproof structural join between the planks.

During the 1960's when stitch and tape boats like the Mirror 11 started to appear on the market, the seams were made up of glass woven roving tape and Polyester type 'A' resin. This resin is still sometimes used due to it's low cost and the ease with which it can often be obtained but, to be honest, I have not used it for many years because although much more expensive, epoxy resins offer many advantages over the Polyester resins.

The advantages of the epoxy resins over the polyester resins are that they adhere much better to the wood, they do not shrink on curing and try and pull away from the wood and they cure harder providing a better surface for higher standards of finish, Also epoxy soaked into the wood provides a much better and longer lasting barrier to water and is much stronger in tension and compression, especially when 'filled' with various modifying powders and will therefore structurally fill gaps and form a very strong glue. Epoxies may suffer if subject to ultra-violet light and therefore they do need protection from direct sunlight. They are also a good deal more expensive than Polyester resins. But Polyester resins are still available and are often used for canoe and small dinghy building and so we will look at how they are used first.

7.2 Stitch & Tape using Polyester Resin

As we have already said, Polyester resins are not as strong as epoxy resins and so it is usually necessary to retain the stitches in place whilst the inside of the seams, which are tackled first, are glass taped.

Before applying the woven roving tape to the inside of the chine seam, prepare the seam first by hammering the wire into the seam so that it presents less of a bump (Figure 26) and by scoring the ply lightly where the tape will go to produce a mechanical bond for the tape (Figure 27).

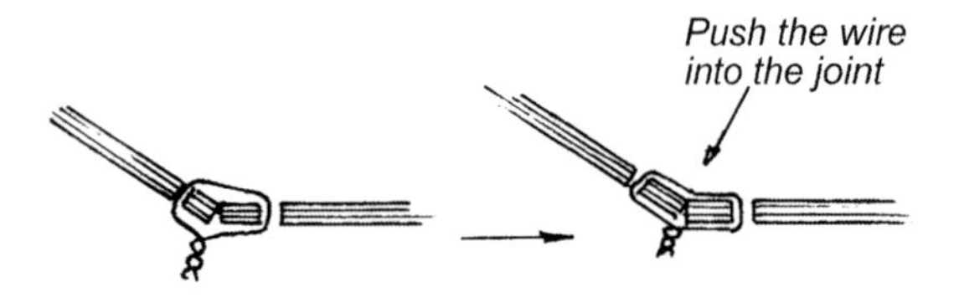

Fig 26. Push the wire into the seam so that it causes a small bump.

Use the edge of a screw driver to do this, a chisel raises the wood fibres too much and prevents the tape from lying down flat. Having done this, prime the surface of the wood with the Polyester/hardner (sometimes called fiberglass) resin. Wood soaks up a lot of resin and will drain resin away from the

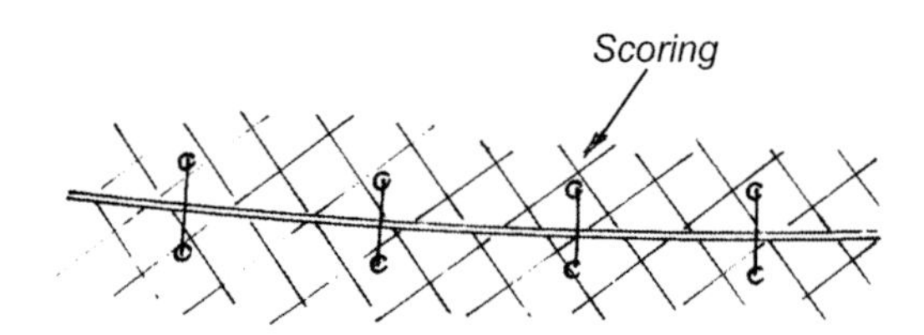

Fig 27. Score the area to increase the mechanical bond between tape and plywood.

tape causing a weak joint. Allow this priming coat to cure before applying the tape with more resin. The tape should be thoroughly ‘wetted’ out (soaked) leaving no dry areas. When the tape is good and wet you will note that it changes from it’s normally white colour and becomes transparent so that you can see the wood surface through it.

Some builders use rollers for this purpose, but I prefer to use a 1 1/2’’ (38mm) brush which allows me to really stipple the resin into the tape. Use brushes which have an unpainted handle as the resin and cleaner will attack the normal paint finish on a brush and the colour will get mixed up with the resin that you apply.

Again, before applying the tape, fill any gaps with a mixture of resin and filler powder (grey talc is the most common). Mix in enough to form a thick putty having first put in extra hardener.

When applying the resin primer you may wish to put some masking tape either side of the seam to prevent the resin spreading too far. Take the tape off (by pealing it back on it’s self) before the resin has cured (Figure 28).

The resin you should use for the taping is General Purpose Type ‘A’ resin which usually requires 5cc of catalyst per lb. to harden it (but check the suppliers literature).

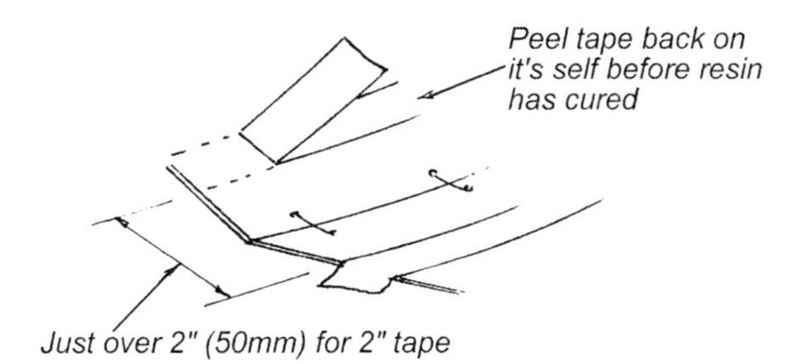

Fig 28. Taping each side of the join to prevent resin from spreading too far.

You can use slightly more catalyst, say 8 cc in cold conditions or when you are mixing fillers with the resin and the catalyst should be thoroughly mixed with the resin first before you add the fillers.

I usually make up resin and catalyst in large yogurt cartons. If you fill these to about 3/4 of their volume this is about 3/4 lb of resin, but check this for yourself. Make a large black mark with a crayon on the outside of the carton and you can refill accurately to the same level each time.

When using the resin, keep it on the move in the carton all the time by stirring it with the brush each time you reload the brush. You will find that the heat from your hand will cause the resin in the carton to cure very quickly and stirring it slows this process down. It is sometimes a good idea to pour part of the catalysed resin into a wider container so that you spread it's volume and this will slow it's cure. If you mix up too much resin and catalyst in one go it will cure fast in the container because of the bulk heat reaction.

Make sure that the catalyst is thoroughly mixed through the resin (you usually see the resin change from pink to a darker colour when it is mixed) but do not be tempted to use too much catalyst as I have found that it tends to make the resin too brittle. Use a special measuring bottle to measure out the catalyst, or a syringe.

Do make sure that you are properly set up before you start with:

- Acetone for cleaning the brushes and yourself.
- Plenty of large yogurt/pot noodle (I am not asking you to eat the stuff!) type containers.
- Mixing sticks.
- Cheap 1'' (25mm) and 1 1/2'' (38mm) brushes.
- Large syringes for measuring out the catalyst.
- Barrier cream and disposable surgical type gloves.

2'' (50mm) 8 oz. tape is sufficient for the seams of most canoes up to 16' (4.8m) in length made of 3/16" or 1/4'' (4-6mm) ply. Use 3'' (75mm) tape or 2 layers of slightly overlapping 2'' (50mm) tape for highly stressed areas (Figure 29).

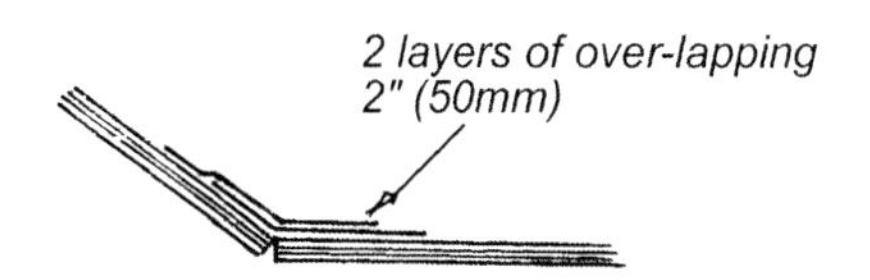

Fig 29. Using 2 layers of W.R. glass tape on highly stressed areas.

Once the inside of the seam has cured, turn the boat over and cut the wires off flush with the ply (use snips and a file or a hacksaw blade) (Figure 30). Plane and fill the seam and prepare as for the inside of the seam before applying the tape.

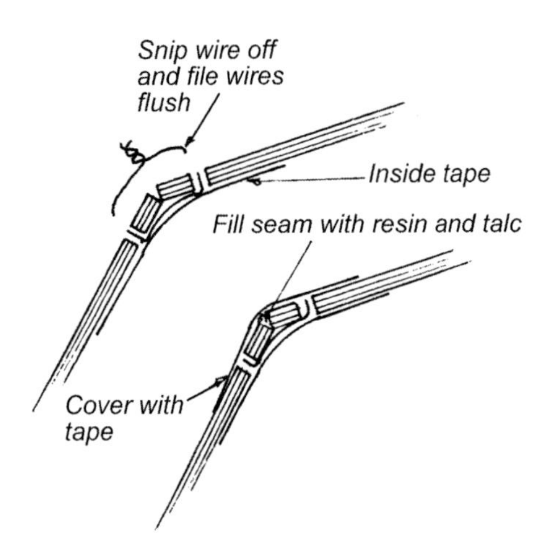

Fig 30. Finishing the outside of the stitch and tape seam.

7.3 Stitch & Tape using Epoxy Resin

Because of the gap filling and glue strength of epoxy resins when they are modified by mixing them with various filler powders, we can often use them to bond the hull planks together so that most of the stitches can be removed before taping begins. This leaves a much neater chine seam but I would not do this with boats that use Polyester resins in their construction. The stitches at the bow which are often under a fair amount of stress are left in place and simply covered when thickened epoxy is applied.

The idea is to 'spot-weld' the panel seams with small amounts of thickened resin in between the stitches. The thickened resin can be applied to both the inside of the seam and to the 'V gap on the outside of the seam—Figure 31. Once this has cured, the stitches can be entirely removed leaving a surface on the inside of the seam free of all the stitches which would cause bumps in the glass tape. This process of course, takes more time, but is well worth doing if you want to produce a clean interior.

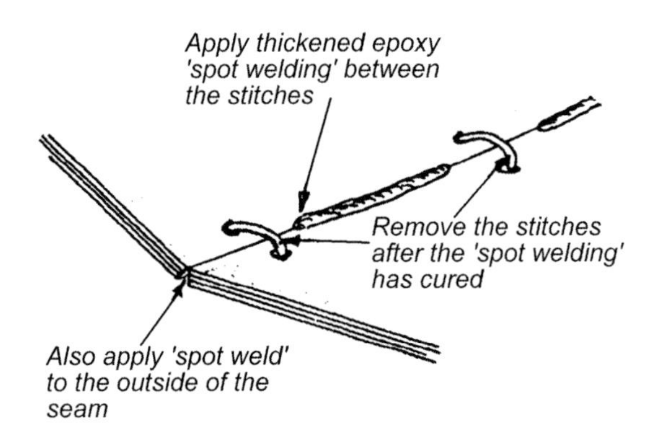

Fig 31. Applying thickened epoxy 'spot welds' to the seam so that the stitches can be removed.

For the thickening the epoxy resin I use WEST407 which is a lightweight filler and works well in most applications as a filler for epoxy glue and for fairing—this is a blend of several different fillers. Mix with the resin until you get a fairly thick mixture of ''Mayonnaise'' consistency which will hold it's shape in a lump, but where peaks will slowly fall over (Figure 32).

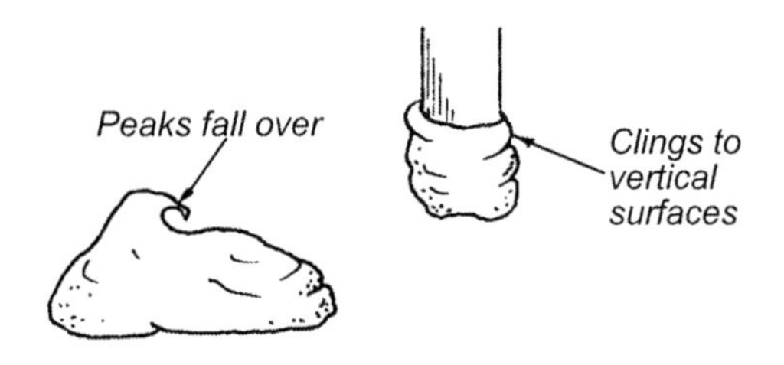

Fig 32. The test of a good filleting mix.

The equipment required is similar to that used for Polyester resins except that I always use the 'mini pumps' supplied by the resin manufacturer to accurately measure out the resin and hardener which is often in a 5:1 mix of resin to hardener.

Having allowed the epoxy fillets to cure and

removed all the stitches, you can, lightly sand down the seams and carefully clean all saw dust and debris out from the interior of the hull. Now, starting with the centerline seam and working your way up, lay out and cut the lengths of glass tape. In most canoes you can remove bulkheads and replace them with braces across the beam to keep the hull in it's correct shape. This allows you to run your chine tapes right through from bow to stern.

Above—laying out and cutting the W.R. tapes for a Hazelnut canoe.

Having cut the tape lengths, carefully remove and stack the tapes in order leaving you with the centreline tape to hand—*Note, cutting and laying out your tapes this way applies to hulls using Polyester resin too.*

With epoxies, I find that there is no need to 'prime' the seam first—so, apply the resin/hardener mix using a brush to the seam and then apply the tape from one end, gently pulling and stretching it into a straight line over the seam. The epoxy resin will start to wet the tape out and as it does so I quickly go over it with the brush, to help. Do not apply more resin yet but go to the next seam (the first chine seam) and repeat the process there. Having applied the first of the chine seam tapes, go back to the centerline seam tape and apply more resin to it if required to wet it out completely.

Above—the W.R. tape on the centreline seam starting to 'wet out'.

Continue this process until all the chine seams have been taped. Do not apply too much resin or you will end up with resin drips and runs. Once cured, turn the hull over and fill the outside seams with thickened epoxy, clean up and apply the outside tapes.

Below—the outside chine seams have been taped and now the tape is being applied to the bow—it has to have cuts each side so that it will go round the curve—the tape is allowed to overlap—these are ground flat later.

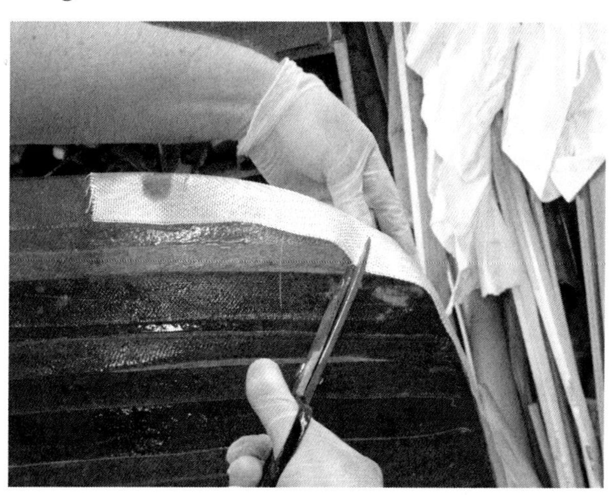

7.4 Omitting the Tapes on the Outside of the Chine Seams

When using epoxies (as opposed to polyester resins) for stitch and tape construction on canoes, I have started to omit the glass tape on the outside of chine seams (Figure 33).

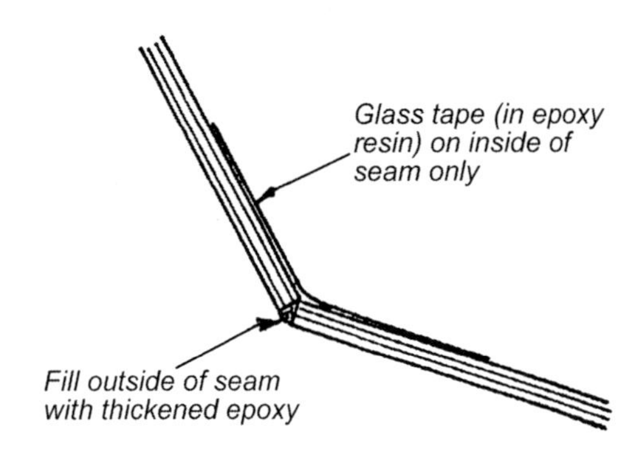

Fig 33. Taping the inside of the chine seam only and simply filling the outside of the seam with thickened epoxy.

Our family canoe for many years was one of my Christine designs which has four planks per side. This craft has given sterling service without any sign of movement in the chine seams despite being dropped and generally mishandled. She has tape on the inside seams and on the outside of the centreline seam only, with the remaining seams on the outside simply filled with thickened epoxy.

Where the hull panels meet each other with no angle, or little angle between them (for instance on the topsides, towards the bow), there is no where to put any thickened epoxy. In this case, a 'groove' of some sort needs to be created to accommodate the epoxy filleting (*note—I do not bother to create a groove on canoes that will be lightly used or which have more than 4 planks per side).*

I have done this in one of two ways, either by using a router to create a rebate in the edges of the panels (Figure 34), or by planing a bevel on the edges (Figure 35).

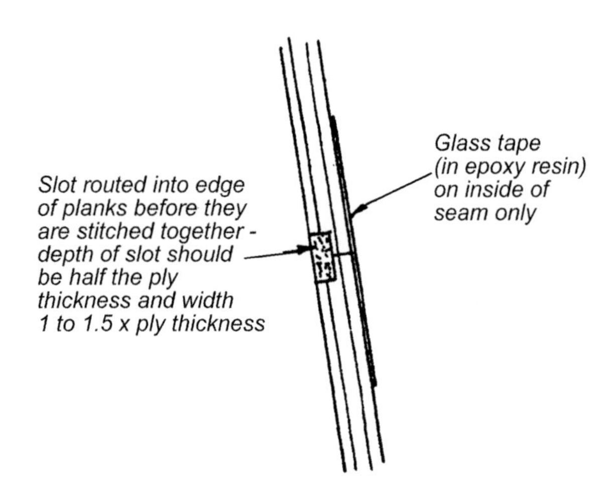

Fig 34. Routed slot used to accommodate the epoxy fillet when the planks are in-line with each other.

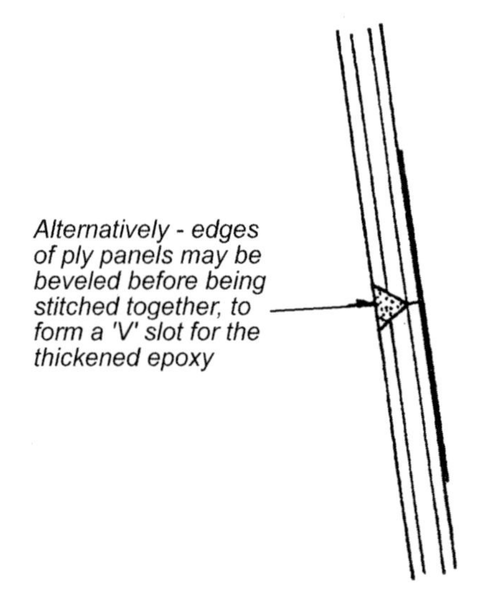

Fig 35. A 'V' gap used for the same purpose.

You can sometimes gauge whether the planking will need a slot, from the shape of the forward frame or bulkhead given on the plans. However, the only true way to see where this maybe necessary, is to stitch the panels together first. This will mean unstitching in order to route or plane the groove up. Do not try routing 'on the job' with the planks stitched up! I have tried this and the router insists on taking any route but the one you want it to take. So take the time to unstitch before attempting to router or plane.

7.5 Eliminating Tape Bumps on the Outside of the Chine Seam

Where, due to it's size or type, a canoe definitely needs tapes on the outside of the chines, I often get asked whether it is possible to construct a stitch and tape canoe without having the 'bump' created by the glass tape on the chine seams. The ply thickness used for canoes is often too thin to think of routing out the outside veneer to sit the tape in and therefore the answer is the use of lightweight epoxy fillers carefully sanded down —see Chapter 9.

7.6 Bonding Plywood Frames/Bulkheads to the Hull

Once the chine seams have been taped we can bond the plywood frames/bulkheads into place. I like to fit the ply frames over the taped seams, but if this is not possible, the chine tapes simply need to stop either side of the ply frame. In any case, the epoxy fillets used to bond the frames in place (Figure 36) are applied over the chine seam tape. The epoxy fillets are usually only of small size—around 3/8" (9mm) radius is all that is usually required. Use masking tape applied before the fillet and removed before the fillet has cured, to keep the join neat (Figure 37).

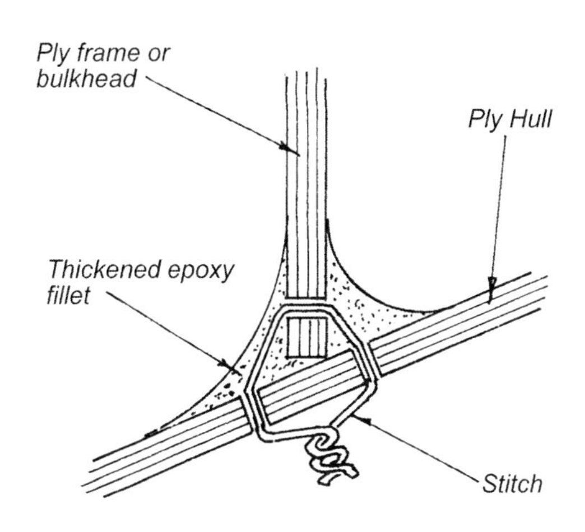

Fig 36. Epoxy filleting frames into the hull.

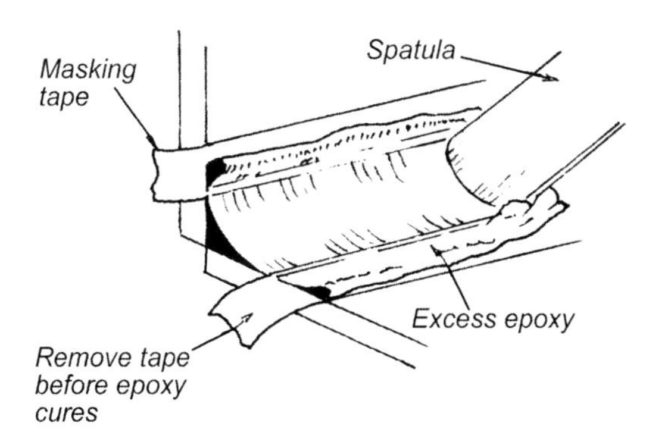

Fig 37. Making a neat epoxy seam.

More often than not, I leave the stitches holding the frames to the hull, in place, as the hull panels often try to pull away from the frame—the epoxy fillet simply hides these stitches.

If the stem and any transom are also epoxy filleted in place, this is the time to do this job, again applying the fillets over the ends of the chine seam tapes.

7.7 General Notes on Epoxies

Epoxies are fairly high tech' materials and have been designed to be used in more or less ideal conditions. If you are building a boat from scratch with new timber, this should present few problems as the wood that you will be using should have a moisture content of around 12% anyway. Most epoxies are mixed together in a 1:5 ratio of hardener to resin by weight. This mix should not be deviated from and care should be taken in measuring out the quantities. Rather than measuring with syringes etc I now almost always use the 'mini' pumps that you can get for the epoxy resins.

Epoxies should be used in dry conditions of low humidity (below 65%) where a temperature of around 15 C (60 F) can be maintained. I have worked in conditions with epoxies which have been far from ideal but be careful and if you have any doubt, contact the manufacturer's for advice.

For most applications, I find that using the resin with a fast hardener is fine if the temperature is not too high. The slow hardener allows you more time for adjustment and for rectifying mistakes. The advantage of the fast hardener is that it has a workable cure of around 6 hours.

To keep costs down, I tend to use Marine adhesives (Cascamite, Aerolite 306, Balcotan etc) for most gluing jobs. Using conventional glues for gunwales, thwarts etc is perfectly alright but you may wish to take advantage of the high strength and gap filling properties of epoxies for bonding and gluing items which are subjected to high stress.

Above—masking tape being used on the outside of the seams so that they can be filled with thickened epoxy from the inside.

Above—thickened epoxy has been applied in between the stitches to 'spot weld' the planks together along the chines—note how the frames/ bulkheads and temporary central mould have been kept in place to retain the correct hull shape.

Below—a frame/bulkhead refitted over the glassed chine seams ready to be epoxy filleted in place—note the masking tape to help produce a neat fillet.

Chapter 8

FITTING OUT THE HULL

WITH GUNWALES, THWARTS (SEATS) & DECKING

8.1 General

Having completed the chine (plank) seams and bonded in any plywood frames/ bulkheads, we can start to look at fitting the hull out with thwarts (seats), decking etc. All of these components will, in a modern stitch and tape canoe, have the secondary function of adding strength and stiffness to the hull and I usually start with the component which adds most to the stiffness of the hull and that is the gunwales. *For the parts of a modern plywood canoe see page 3.*

8.2 The Gunwales

The gunwales are the longitudinal pieces of wood attached to the top edge of the plywood planking. They often consist of two pieces, the 'inwales' on the inboard side of the planking and the 'outwale' on the outboard side of the planking and together, they sandwich the top edge of the uppermost plank (Figure 38).

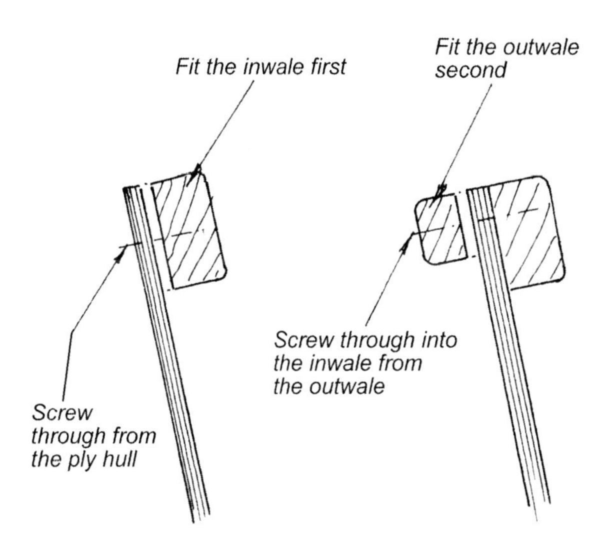

Fig 38. Fitting the inwale and outwale.

Fit the inwale first—I lay the first inwale onto the hull and roughly mark the shape for one end—note that it needs to fit the shape of the inside of the bow and to fit against the inwale on the opposite side of the canoe (Figure 39).

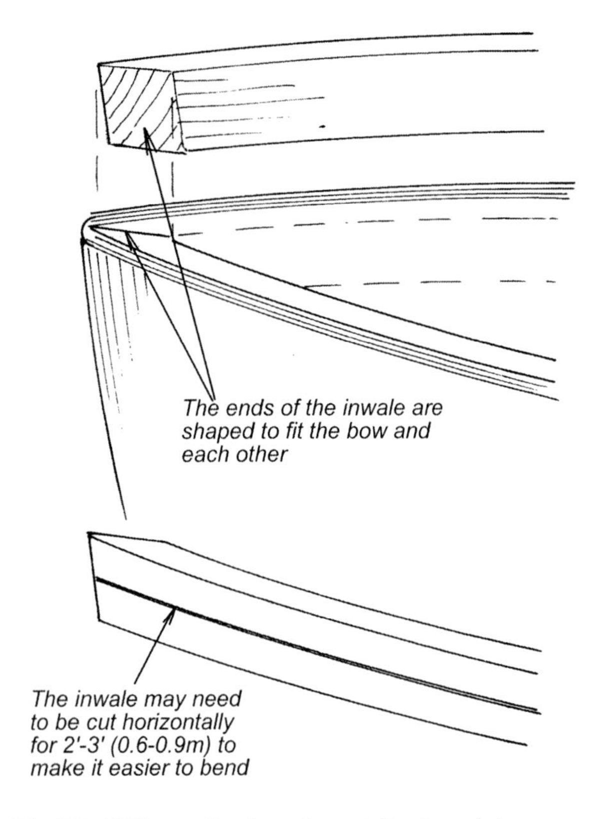

Fig 39. Fittings the inwales at the bow/stern.

The join between the two inwales will usually be hidden, so a completely neat and tight join here is not necessary. Sometimes, due to the curve of the gunwale at the bow/ stern, especially with the traditional scooped up Canadian style of bow, it is impossible to bend the inwale into shape. You have two alternatives in this case— either taper the inwale down to a smaller size as it goes towards the ends by reducing it's width and thickness or, cut it with a saw horizontally for a few feet (a metre or so) so that you will effectively be laminating it.

Having achieved the correct shape at one end, I then spring the inwale into place until it overhangs the other end, roughly clamp it in place and then mark and cut it.

Having fitted one inwale, I screw this in place (from the outside of the ply plank) and cut and fit the inwale on the opposite side again screwing it into place. Mark across the top edge of the plank and inwales at various different places so that when you remove and apply glue, you can get the inwales back into their correct positions. I screw every 10" (250mm) using 5/8" x 8G (15mm x 8G) steel screws. After the glue has cured these screws are removed.

The outwale can then be fitted—shape one end first and clamp into place so that you can mark the other end—remove and cut and then dry screw with 1" x 8G (25mm x 8G) brass screws again at 10" (250mm) spacing. Screw right through to the inwale. Remove the screws, coat the inboard face with glue and re-screw.

The inwale has been fitted roughly in place and held with cramps so that one end can be marked—the inwale is then removed, cut and offered back up to see how it fits—remember that it needs to be cut so that the opposite inwale will fit against it.

Note how the inwale will not bend up to conform to the top of the plank—because this is happening right forward under the deck, it is not too important especially since the plank and inwale will be cut down to accommodate the plywood deck—see 8.3.

8.3 The Breast Hook or Deck

At the bow and stern, we need something which will stiffen and strengthen the angle between the hull sides and inwales. If you are going to fit a water-tight compartment or storage area in the ends of the canoe, this can be a simple plywood deck. If you are not going to fit such an area then we can fit, what is effectively a small open deck in the form of a horizontal triangular plywood knee which is called a breast hook.

The easiest way to fit either a ply deck or breast hook is to place a piece of oversized ply on top of the gunwales, mark round it, remove it and cut it to shape and then refit with glue and screws. However, this is not very neat and leaves the edge of the plywood deck/breast hook exposed. With a little more effort we can fit a much smarter deck or breast hook simply by cutting the top of the inwale and plank down by the thickness of the plywood deck. The deck/breast hook is then glued and fastened and the outwale fitted to cover the edge (Figure 40).

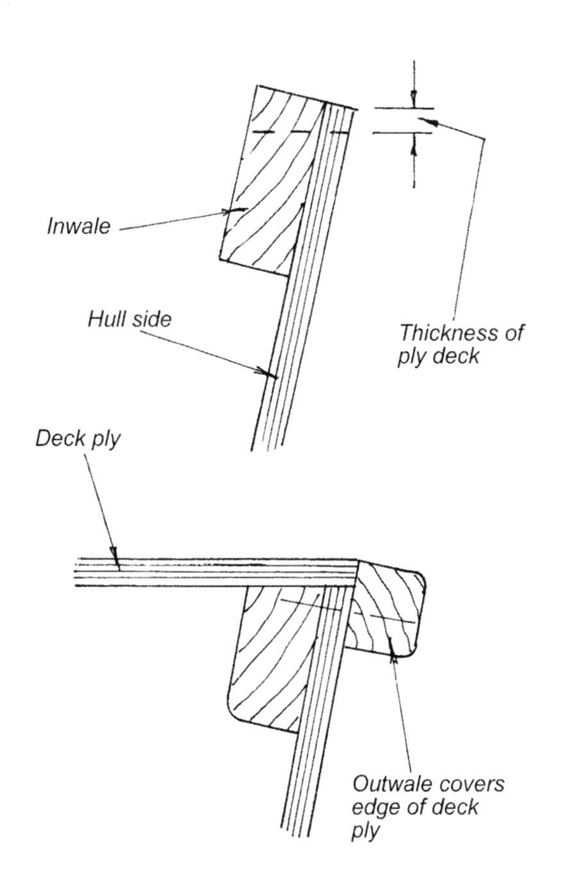

Fig 40. Setting a plywood deck or breasthook down flush with the top of the gunwale to cover the exposed edge of the plywood.

To cut the inwale/plank down for the deck/ breasthook, mark the thickness of the plywood being used for the deck/ breast hook along the top edge of the plank, decide how far back the deck/ breast hook is going to come, cut across at this point and start to remove the excess material with a chisel.

Much of the excess material can also be removed with the jig-saw.

If you are fitting compartments into the ends of the canoe the top of the plywood bulkhead which forms the end of the compartment will need a beam so that you have something to secure the decking to.

For most canoes this can simply be a piece of timber which is butted against the inboard faces of the inwales but, if you wish to make a proper job of it, the ends of the beam are cut with a 'slope' which is housed into the inwale—Figure 41. Although I do this on larger boats, I rarely do it on canoes as the additional strength given by it to the inwale/ beam join, is simply not needed.

A simple beam at the top of the bulkhead butted against the inboard faces of the inwales.

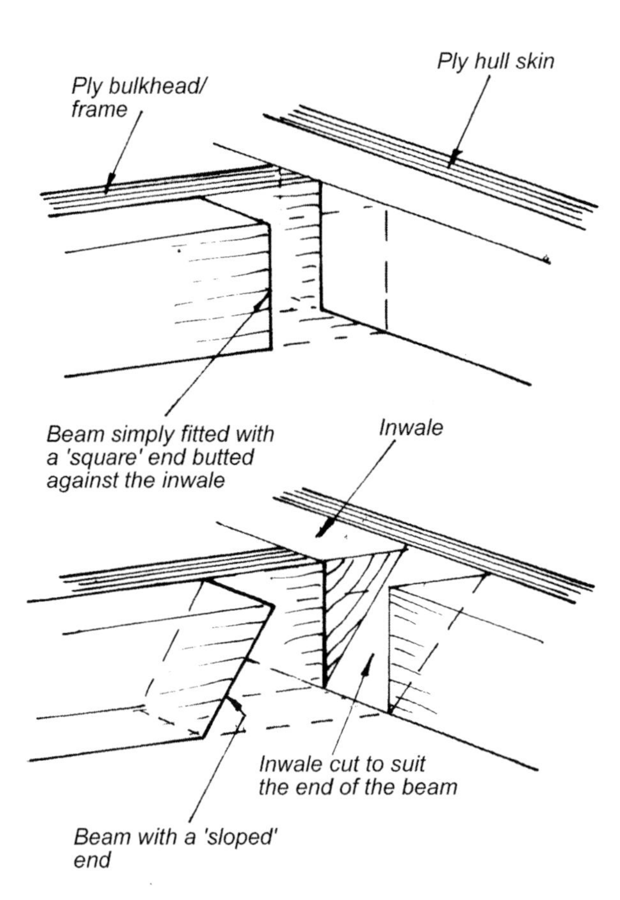

Fig 41. Fitting the beam at the top of the bulkhead between the inwales.

Above—the deck which was cut slightly over-size has been glued and fastened in place and the edges are now being trimmed back to be flush with the planking.

Above—the outwales being fitted to cover the edge of the decking.

8.4 The Stretcher/Yoke

Before fitting seats etc I usually fit the stretcher/yoke. The stretcher is simply a piece of timber fitted between the gunwales which stiffens the sides of the canoe and prevents the sides from flexing in and out (panting). It can also form a yoke which is often a beautifully sculptured piece of timber, again fastened between the gunwales and which is used to help carry the canoe—see 12.6.

I tend to use a piece of 1"x2" (25x50mm) timber with it's corners rounded off cut to fit the widest part of the canoe just under the inwales. Fixing it is simply a matter of screwing through from the outside of the hull into each end and gluing with thickened epoxy (Figure 42).

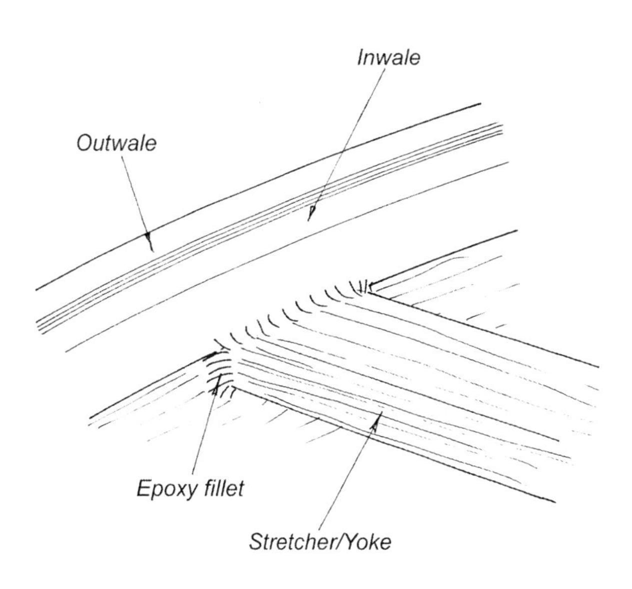

Fig 42. Fitting a simple stretcher/yoke.

8.5 Seats/Thwarts

With the inwales fitted and stiffened with the stretcher, we can turn our attention to the fitting of the seats/thwarts. The fore and aft positions and height of the seats will be given on the drawings and these positions should now be carefully marked onto the inside of the canoe. Having the canoe level at this stage is a good idea.

No matter what type of seats/thwarts we are going to fit, we want to find the length of the seats at the their fore and aft edges. To do this, I use 'pinch rods' which are two pieces of wood held together with tape after they have been pushed out to the marks made on the inside of the hull (Figure 43).

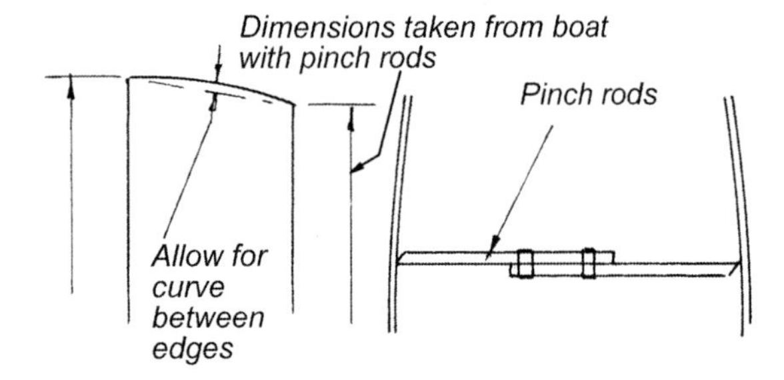

Fig 43. Using 'pinch rods' to find the length of the seats.

There are several different types of seats that you can use. The simplest is a plywood seat supported by wood stiffeners along it's fore and aft edges which is screwed and epoxy filleted into place (Figure 44).

Fig 44. A simple plywood seat.

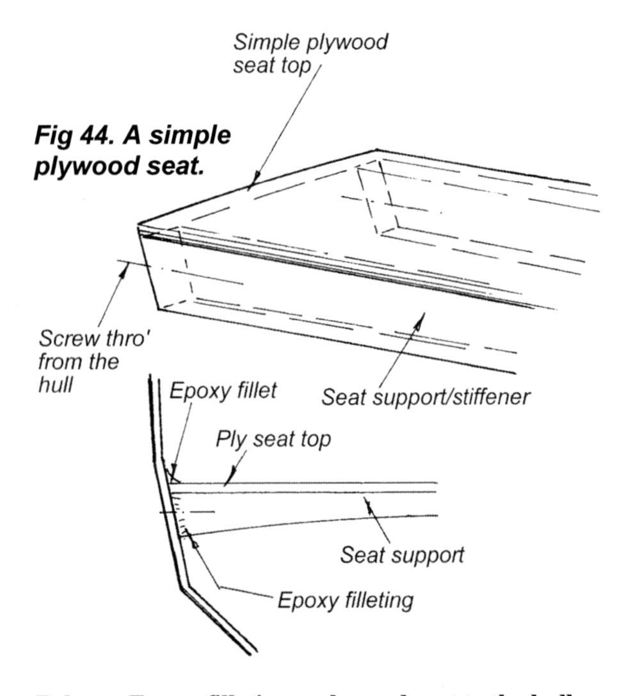

Below—Epoxy filleting a plywood seat to the hull.

I have also made up a seat from dowel—1 1/4" (30m) dia. for the main pieces and 3/8" or 1/2" (9 or 12m) for the spacers—this forms a rectangle which is epoxied and screwed to the hull and the seat itself is formed from a canvas rectangle—the ends of the rectangle are tensioned together under the seat with lacing through eyeleted holes (Figure 45). Webbing can also be used.

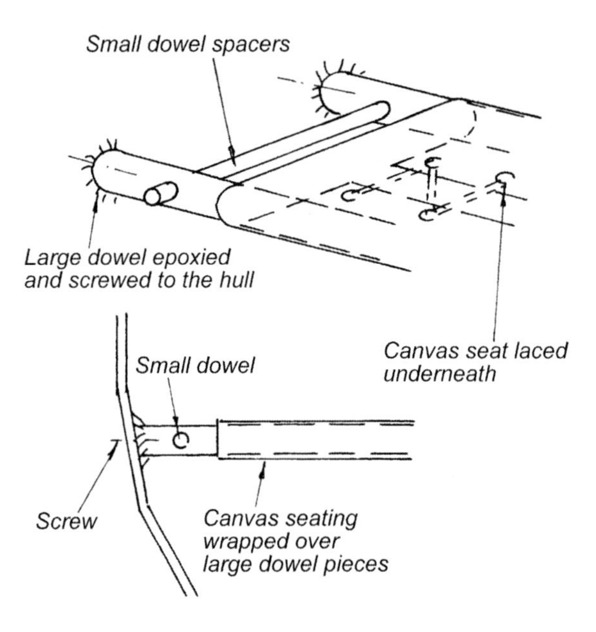

Fig 45. A canvas seat made up with a dowel rod frame.

Above—a Little Kate with a webbed seat—note how the seat frame has been suspended from the inwales by long bolts—this allows some adjustment to seat height. Also, I have found sometimes, that vertical posts are needed between the seat frame and hull bottom to help stiffen the seat.

Chapter 9

PAINTING & FINISHING

INCLUDING SHEATHING THE HULL

9.1 Painting & Varnishing

There are basically three paint systems that can be used to finish a canoe :-

- 'Conventional' – usually single-pot paints and varnishes.
- 'High Performance' systems – often 2-pot and polyurethane based.
- Epoxy coating which is then paint or varnish finished.

Which one you choose will come down to how much you are prepared to spend and where the boat is to be used. A general purpose canoe, constantly being scrapped on trailers or on the beach, will certainly benefit from a tough high performance paint or varnish, but the finish will quickly be ruined and so the question has to be asked, whether it is worth using a more expensive system under these circumstances.

If you have invested considerably in the cost of the materials, and more so, in the construction time, it is silly not to compliment your boat with a well applied high quality finish.

High Performance systems do need more care taken in their application in terms of the humidity and temperature of the work space but, under normal use, they will keep their gloss longer and last a greater amount of time and protect the canoe better, than conventional systems.

Epoxy coated and glass sheathed canoes do need to be painted or varnished – if varnished, the varnish should have an ultra-violet filter in it as epoxy exposed to sunlight, will degrade over time.

Whichever system you choose, make sure you follow the manufacturer's instructions to the letter – in particular, if the canoe is epoxy coated, make sure that the epoxy is completely cured before applying any paint or varnish. The epoxy surface may feel cured, but it is that last 0.001% of cure which, no matter how ideal the conditions, takes several days to complete that can cause problems. If the cure is not complete, problems will occur for subsequent coatings – either by throwing the paint/varnish off, or by not allowing the paint/varnish to cure at all. Be warned, paint not curing over an epoxy coated surface is a common problem – be patient!

No matter what system you use, the surfaces to be painted or varnished have to be prepared first and yes, it is worth repeating what every skilled painter says, *"in order to get a good finish, preparation is 75% of the battle"* – take your time!

Here is a typical preparation and painting sequence :-

- Search the surfaces to be painted for holes, gaps etc and fill – I use thickened epoxy.
- Once the filler has fully cured, carefully sand down and also search for any other bumps in the surface that need sanding down too – 80 to 100 grit sandpaper is used here. Filling the holes for screw heads is rarely done in one fill and so refill these where necessary and sand again.
- Carefully sand the whole surface with 120 to 180 grit sandpaper finishing off 'with the grain'.
- Spring clean your whole workshop and the canoe itself – be fastidious in searching out and removing all dust and scrap material. If you do this on a sunny day, you will see the amount of dust you have disturbed in the air which will resettle onto the canoe's surface – so clean again.
- On the day that painting starts (and on subsequent painting days) some builders will 'damp down' the building floor etc to prevent dust circulating up.
- Decide on your painting sequence – ie where are you going to paint first – do not paint yourself into a corner. I tend to start on the interior of the canoe first and work my way out.
- If at all possible, do the important painting on dry warm days with little moisture in the air – certainly do not paint early in the morning when there will be dampness in the atmosphere and temperatures are going to rise.
- Paint the first coat of primer (this is often thinned). Use the 'Union Jack' method by using diagonal strokes to spread the paint and then horizontal strokes, finishing off with vertical strokes. Work quickly keeping the working edges 'wet'.
- This first coat is a 'tell-tale' or 'indicator' coat so, when dry, inspect the surface for blemishes and areas that did not show up before, as dips etc and refill and sand again.
- I usually use another coat of primer but go by the paint manufacturer's instructions.
- Sand between coats using 280 to 320 grit paper.
- At least 3 coats of undercoat should be used, sanding between coats – I use 'wet and dry' paper with water at this and subsequent stages.
- At least 2 if not 3 coats of top coat should be applied, again, sanding between coats.

Varnished surfaces use much the same sequence (without the filling) with at least 4 or 5 coats. Epoxy coated surfaces often need to be 'keyed' first with a light sanding, before they are painted.

9.2 Sheathing the Hull

Sheathing is done before any final painting or varnishing. There are two reasons for sheathing your canoe. The first, is to give the outside of the hull an abrasion resistant finish that will also act as a barrier to water and help prevent leaks. The second, is to add strength and stiffness to the hull shell. Sheathing is only done on the outside of the hull and means that you can forget taping the outside chine and centreline seams. I have rarely felt the need to sheath a canoe but if I do sheath, I use a fairly light weight cloth of around 150-190 g/sq.m.

If you are using epoxy resin, once the priming resin has been applied to the bare plywood, if the surface looks dull and matt, then let it cure hard and sand. If however, the surface remains glossy, then you can apply the cloth straight onto the priming resin after it has only partially cured. If you have large voids to fill in the surface of the hull, let the resin cure and then fill with a resin putty before proceeding with the sheathing.

There are basically two methods for applying the cloth. The 'wet' and 'dry' methods. The 'wet' method requires that you apply resin to the wood surface first and then lay the cloth onto it rolling it down with split washer rollers. The problem here, is that you have to work fast in order to get the whole piece of cloth that you are working on, thoroughly wetted out before the resin starts to cure. This means having a team to help you. If you are working on vertical surfaces, this is really the only way to do it. If you are using epoxies, then use the slow hardener for the 'wet' method.

The 'dry' method entails holding the cloth into position with some tape, and then working resin into the cloth from above ensuring that it becomes well wetted out with no dry areas. This method is easier, in that, it allows you to work at your own pace without having to rush in order to wet the cloth out before all the previously applied resin cures but it cannot be used on vertical surfaces and you must ensure a thorough wetting out of the cloth and the removal of all air bubbles.

Work from the centre of the cloth in both cases using split washer rollers and squeegees (foam covered rollers). Do not over work an area especially with epoxy as this will tend to create bubbles in the resin. I tend to lay the cloth in two pieces, overlapping them along the centreline.

If you need to join the cloths then overlap them and cut—to do this, overlap the cloths slightly, and when the resin has partially cured, use a scalpel to cut a line through both cloths (Figure 46). The piece of cloth underneath can then be removed along with the excess piece on the top and the two cloths smoothed down exactly butting each other.

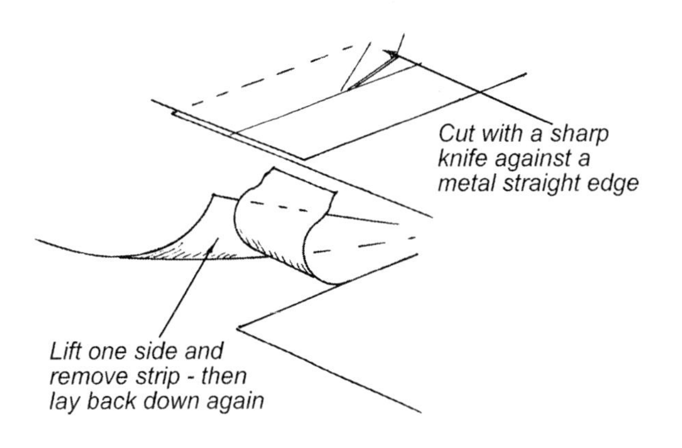

Fig 46. Cutting butts in the cloth.

You should also sheath the hull before you fit runners and rubbing strakes etc., and fasten them over the sheathing so that they help to retain the sheathing (Figure 47).

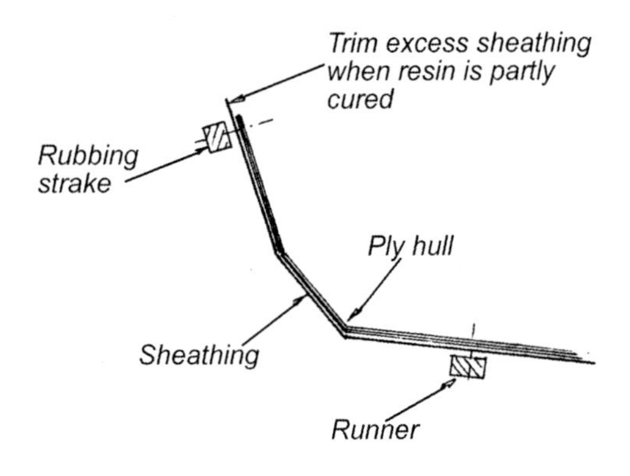

Fig 47. Fitting the strakes and rubbers after sheathing.

Above—12' Outboard Canoe

The photographs on this page are all of finished canoes from the Selway Fisher stable.

Above—12' Adirondack. Below—14' Esk

Above—Dart 14

Above—Baby Raven. Right—Little Kate

Chapter 10

PADDLES

10.1 General

Paddles are a very personal thing, your likes and dislikes being influenced by weight, length, size and shape of the blade and how much water you get up your arm!

The subject is full of controversy and my basic thought, is to experiment and to go for what you find most comfortable and efficient to use.

There are many paddles on the market using aluminium or hybrid fibre shafts with plastic blades and my experience is that they are usually quite efficient giving good power with low fatigue. Their price is also quite reasonable and therefore there is often no need to make your own paddle.

However, I offer here some thoughts on, and drawings of, the sort of paddles that I find enjoyable to use.

10.2.1 The Double Paddle

For touring, a length of 96" (2.44m) is the average, with individual variations of plus or minus 10" (250mm). An 86" (2.18m) paddle is excellent for small open canoes like our Little Kate design, but for kayaks a paddle as short as this needs and produces a quick rate of paddling which will tire you and keep you wet.

Much over 96" (2.44m) and I find that too much effort is required in paddling because of the greater leverage required. Overall, a paddle obviously needs to be well balanced and should not weigh more than a couple of pounds (Figure 48). Some people like a little 'spring' to the shaft which cushions your

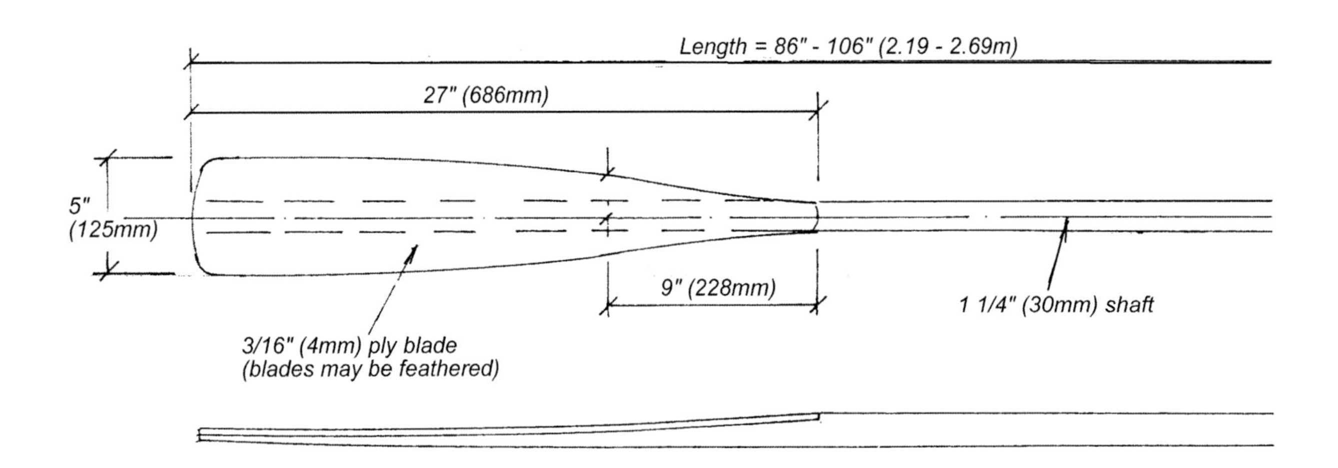

Fig 48. A typical double paddle.

muscles. Too much spring however, will take power out of your stroke. Aluminium shafts are rigid and therefore, to get spring, the shaft needs to be made of grp or wood.

The average diameter of the shaft at the points at which it is gripped is between 1 1/8'' and 1 1/4'' (28 and 31mm). The diameter is quite critical, much less and the paddle springs too much and is weak and also produces a difficult grip (Figure 49).

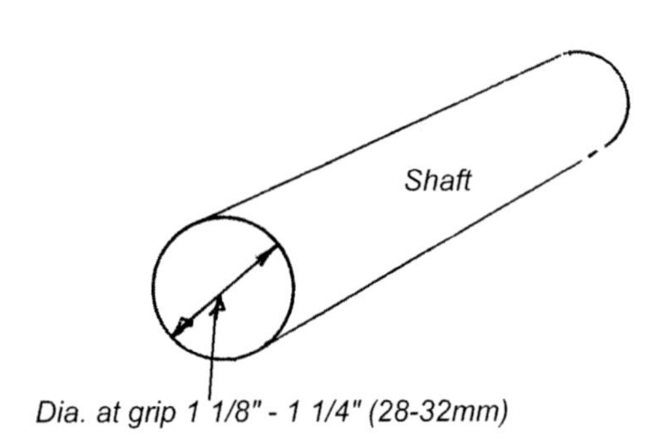

Fig 49. Shaft size for a double paddle.

10.2.2 Blade Design for Double Bladed Paddles

This is a very critical area and is open to much experimentation. Care must be taken to produce a blade that does not 'flutter', ie., one that weaves from side to side during the power stroke. This is a tiring problem and takes control away from your stroke.

The distribution of blade area either side of the shaft is a subject that is often talked about, but I find that spoon bladed paddles are often the best device for overcoming the problem of flutter putting much of the blade on the aft (back) side of the shaft (Figure 50).

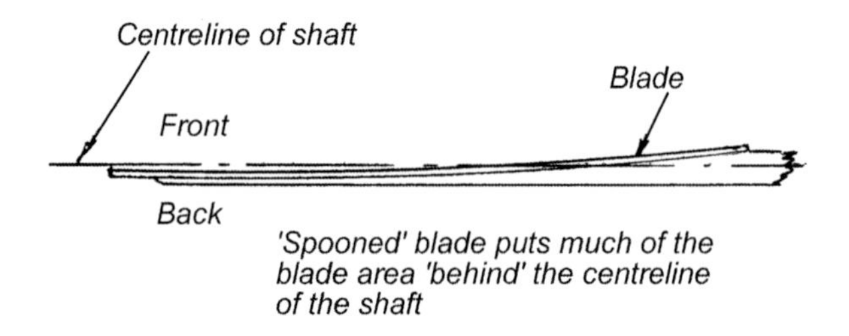

Fig 50. The 'spooned' blade.

The blades of white water canoes are usually short and fat, say 10'' wide x 14''

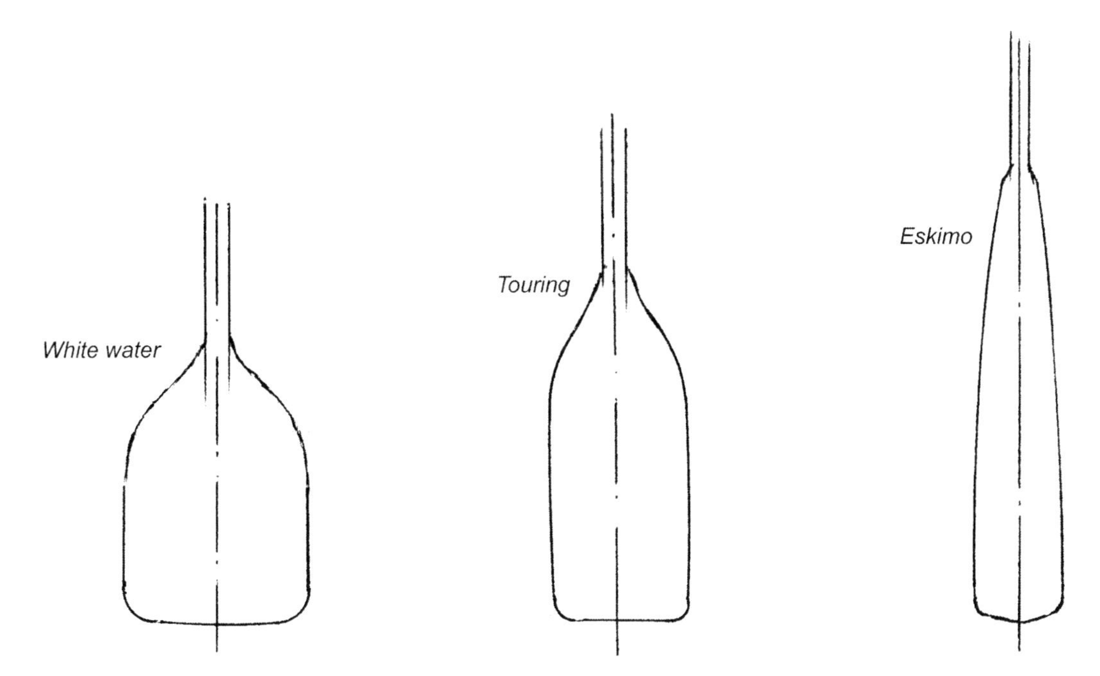

Fig 51. Differences in blade shape.

long (250 x 355mm), whilst a blade for touring may be around 7-8'' wide and 18'' long (175-200 x 450mm). Eskimo blades which may be flat are often 4 1/2''x 27'' (112 x 685mm). Both of the latter blades give a blade area of around 125 sq. ins. (760 sq.cm.). The white water blade is slightly more than this (Figure 51).

Whether you go for a narrow long blade or a wide short one comes down to personal preference and where you canoe (long blades can be frustrating to use in clogged water ways). Although the blade areas may be the same, I find that the short fat blade gives me more control and power.

10.2.3 Feathering

Normal white water paddles are feathered with the blades set at between 70 and 90 degrees to each other so that the out of water blade is parallel to the water, cutting down on wind resistance (Figure 52). Touring paddles for use at sea are usually not feathered because it has been found that this produces difficulties in high winds. From a purely physical point of view, some people do not like to feather their paddles because of the strain that this can cause over a period of time on their wrists and elbow muscles.

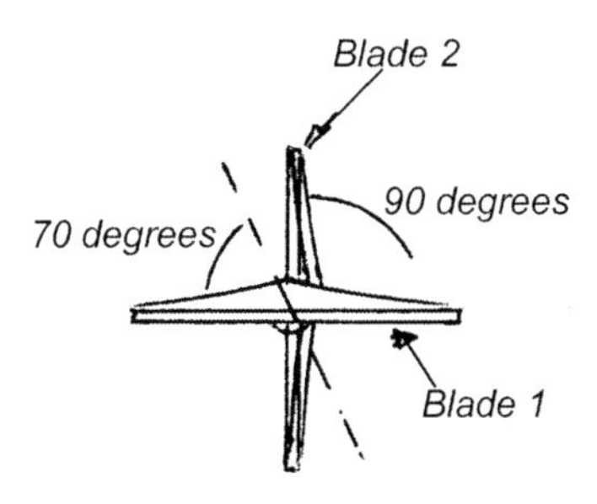

Fig 52. Feathering the blades.

10.3 The Single (Canadian) Canoe Paddle

The single blade or Canadian canoe paddle is subject to a lot of bending stress and therefore it's shape is more often centred around the requirement for strength. Having said that though, the paddle must still be light and with the amount of force used in this type of paddling, fluttering is also a big problem.

I tried many designs until one day, I was hit by a revelation. More accurately, the boat I was sailing in, was hit by a single paddle as it floated down the Clyde somewhere off Dunoon. I recovered the paddle and with no owner any where in sight, I took it home and for several years it remained propping up a corner of my workshop.

Later, I used it on the prototype Waterman 16 design and found that it worked beautifully (Figure 53). So, instead of going into a great discourse here, of the finer points of single blade paddle design, I will simply show details of the design which I still use - it's like your favourite arm chair even whilst falling apart, it is too comfortable to give up.

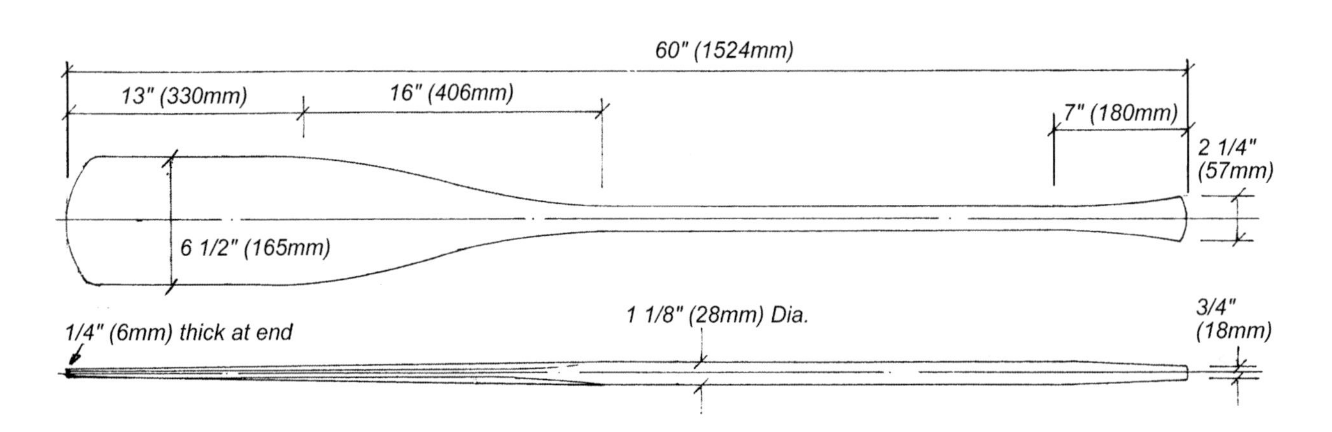

Fig 53. A typical single bladed paddle.

10.4 Making Your Own Paddles

Apart, perhaps, from the shaft, most of the materials used for paddle construction, are from scrap. A single bladed paddle can be made up as shown in Figure 54. I prefer to use Douglas fir for this. Although not the lightest wood, the Fir has less 'spring' and is stronger than both Spruce or Cedar. As you plane up the shaft (using a spoke shave), test it every so often for stiffness. Pieces of wood cut from the same plank will have different strengths and stiffness and much of the success of the single bladed paddle is in the shaft.

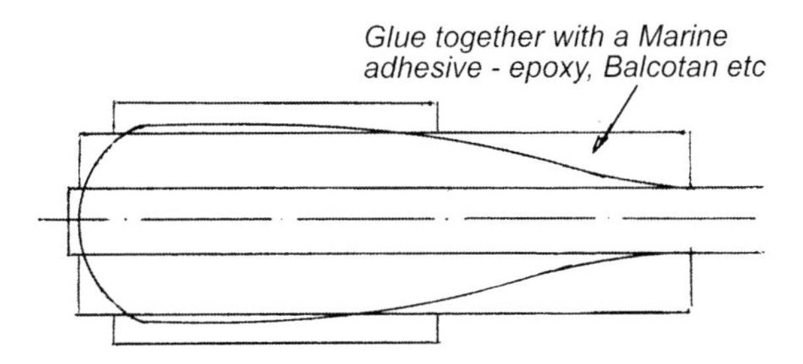

Fig 54. Gluing up the stock for the paddle blade.

For double bladed paddles, I use 1 1/4'' (31mm) Fir for the shaft and 4mm ply for the blades. In order to achieve a good gluing area between the blades and the shaft, cut a flat onto the ends of the shaft (Figure 55). The flat may be cut with a bandsaw but I usually plane it. In order to force the blade into a curve I start off with no flat at the throat of the blade moving to 1/3 the depth of the shaft at around half way along the blade and finishing 1/4 to 1/8 the depth of the shaft at the tip.

Unless you are going to cut the shaft into 2 halves with a brass tube sleeve for the joint, the blades need to be very carefully aligned. For this you need a reference line along the length of the shaft and for this, I use a chalked line which I stretch from one end to the other and snap (pull back and let go) to produce a chalk line on the shaft (Figure 56).

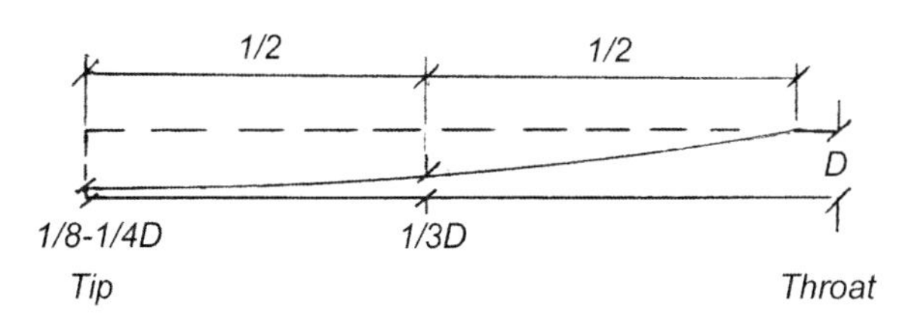

Fig 55. Side view of the 'flat' cut onto the ends of the shaft.

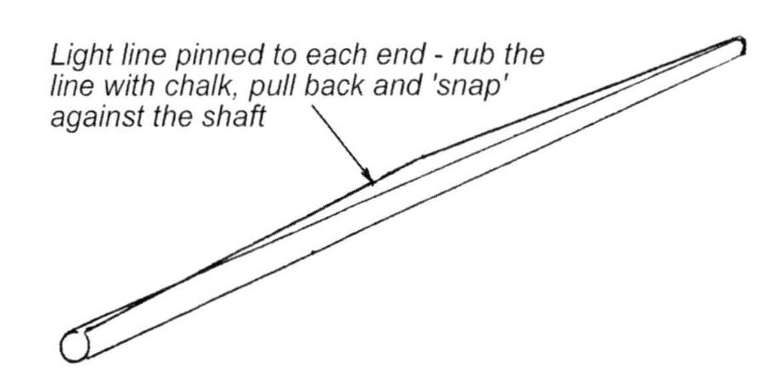

Fig 56. Marking a line on the shaft.

The points of maximum stress on the shaft are where you grip it and at the throat of the blade. Therefore the shaft is usually left parallel sided over it's whole length but tapered from the throat to the tip of the blade (Figure 57).

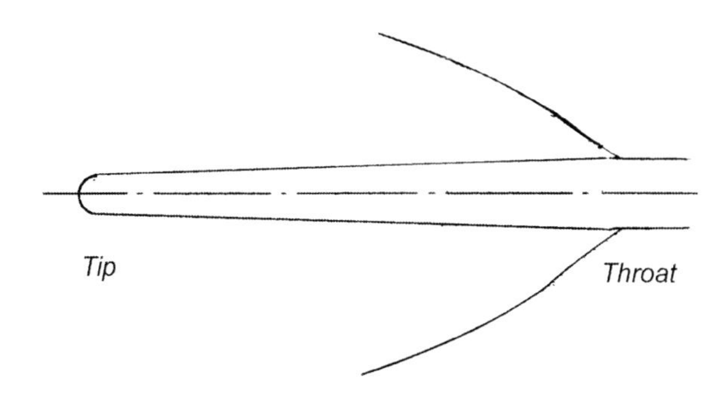

Fig 57. Shaft tapered at ends.

The blades may be made up from pieces of wood glued either side of the shaft and the shape may then be carved out (Figure 58). This is a skilled but very enjoyable process although it does often lead to a heavier paddle. If you wish to construct your paddles in this way, it is better to study such a blade first (if you can find one) and then to construct your own based upon the points raised in this chapter and more importantly your own experience. Paddle design is very much a personal thing!

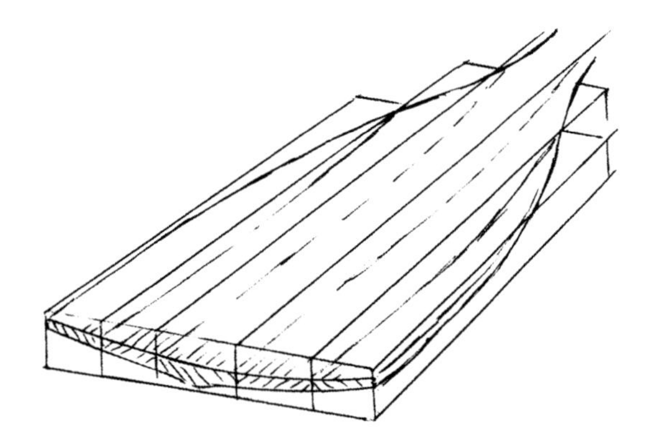

Fig 58. The carved 'spoon' shape found on some paddle blades.

Below—the first 13'9" Christine with three ladies aboard—the paddle in the hands of the forward crew member shows the need to get the length of the loom correct for efficient paddling.

Chapter 11

SAILING RIGS & GEAR FOR CANOES

11.1 General

Many people find the thought of sailing in a canoe quite peculiar, mainly because the thought of sailing in such a small boat which, in comparison to a dinghy, has a small beam, conjures up thoughts of an instant wetting.

Part of the problem, is that the modern sailing fraternity have grown used to the efficient rigs that have been developed over the last 60 or 70 years, or the modern versions of the old working rigs which allow you to sail well to windward and where one never thinks of using anything other than sails for power.

The concept of not sailing when the wind is in the wrong direction, or when conditions are against sailing, or even of using some other form of power at the same time that sails are used, is largely against the norms of modern sailing.

However, if you look at the early use of canoes in Europe and the intrepid journeys of people like MacGregor, much of the time spent in a canoe, if the wind was in the right direction, was spent in sailing, with perhaps a small easily mounted sail. In fact, looking at some of the drawings from such early European craft, the rigs and associated gear became quite sophisticated with fan folding centreboards and fully battened rigs.

I have found that there is nothing quite like gently gliding over the water's surface, lying back in a canoe, with the wind lifting the boat forward, using nature's energy to carry you on your way. Around the next bend, you might find it better to dismount the sailing gear (no hassle if it has been properly designed) because the wind, coming at a different angle now, would mean having to sit uncomfortably on the side of the canoe - a real gentleman's way of canoe cruising this - giving you little respites from having to paddle every mile and the peace and time to observe and take in all around you.

On the other hand, you may hanker after the excitement of hanging out of the side of your canoe as she powers to windward, slicing through the water with spray flying left and right! Whatever you do, adding a sailing rig will transform your canoeing. You may not like it, but why not try - the cost and effort are minimal.

One or two basic points about sailing rigs for canoes. The first covers what you need in the way of additional equipment. You obviously need a sail and something to stick it up on, but you also need two other components. First, something to steer with, which may be a proper stern hung rudder or a paddle held over one side, and second, something to prevent the boat from going sideways - some form of keel.

The 'keel' can be a simple board of ply hung by cord over the canoe's side. Spars (mast and boom) may be made from dowel or broom handle and the sail, because it is light weight, can be made on an ordinary domestic sewing machine from lightweight Terylene or Nylon.

As far as design is concerned, because a canoe is not the most stable craft around, the sail area wants to be kept low in shape and size (Figure 59). Let's look at these items in detail.

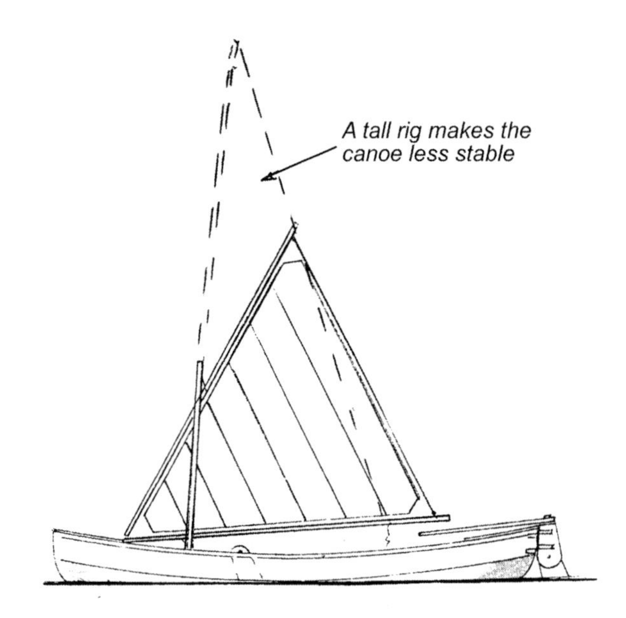

Fig 59. Keeping the height of the rig low.

11.2 The Rudder

Most early canoe sailors simply used a paddle held over one quarter of the boat to steer with and this method is actually more efficient than you might think (Figure 60).

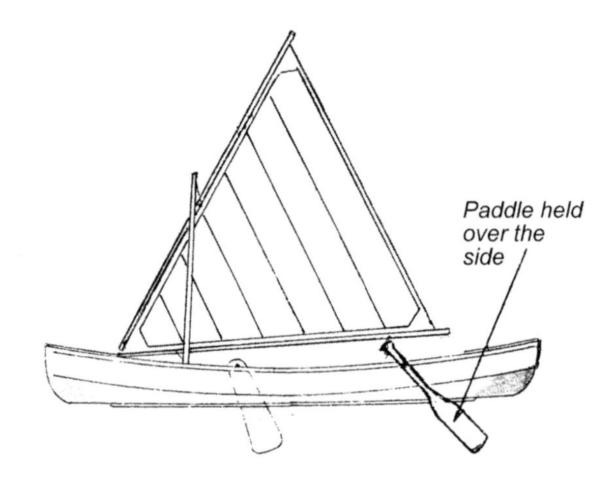

Fig 60. Using a paddle as a simple rudder.

The advantage of steering this way, is that, you do not have any additional special gear to worry about. The disadvantages are a certain loss in efficiency when compared with a normal hinged rudder and the fact that because you do not have a hinge (pintle and gudgeon in normal sailing terms) you have to hold the paddle in place over the side of the boat. In other words, if you let go of the tiller attached to a normal hinged rudder the rudder simply swings about, if you do the same with a paddle and the paddle is not tied into the boat you will loose it overboard.

If you are confident in sailing any way, you should perhaps try using a paddle to see whether you are happy using it. When using this method, I usually have a small rope tied around the shaft and tied to a small cleat with the rope passing over the coaming. This acts as a crude hinge and does prevent you from loosing the oar (Figure 61).

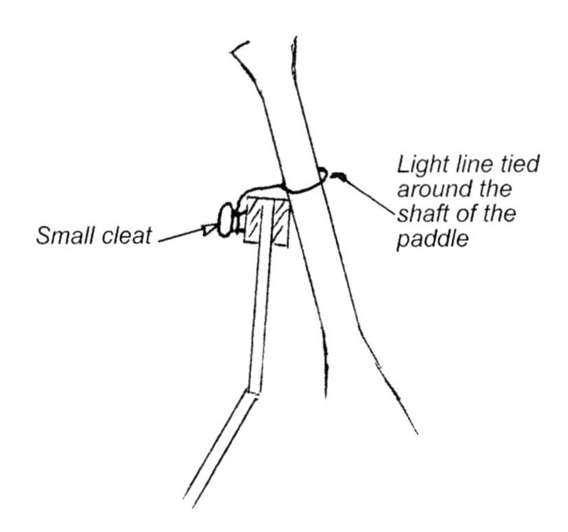

Fig 61. Retaining the paddle/rudder.

If you are not a confident sailor and therefore perhaps liable to get in a 'pickle, you would be better to go for a conventional hinged rudder.

11.2.1 The Hinged Rudder

For a canoe, the rudder needs to be hinged in 2 places rather like rudders found on dinghies.

The first hinge is the one which also attaches the rudder to the canoe and enables the rudder to move from side to side and steer the boat. As already mentioned, this set of hinges are called pintles and gudgeons (Figure 62). These can be brought from a chandlery but can also be easily made. The easiest way to do this is to make four 'U' shaped loops from 1.5mm x 20mm brass strip. These are fastened to the canoe and rudder with through bolts and arranged so that those on the rudder rest on top of those attached to the canoe.

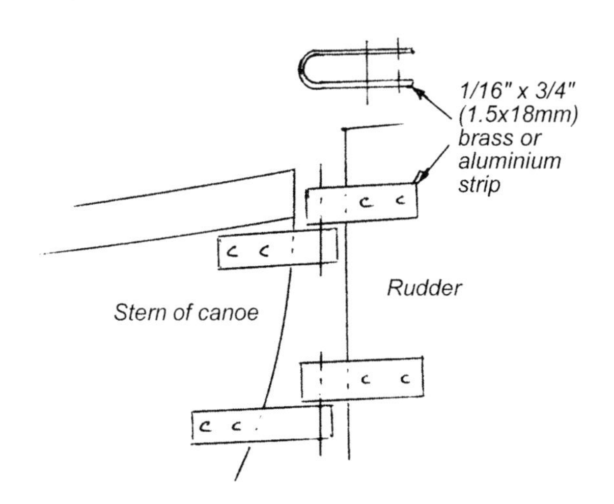

Fig 62. A simple pintle/gudgeon arrangement.

A brass rod pin of 6mm diameter with one end bent over, can then be dropped through the loops to form the hinge pin (Figure 63). Be careful when bending brass, It will need to be annealed (softened) during the bending process or it will fracture (to anneal brass, heat it up until it goes a dull red colour and leave it to cool down by itself). An alternative to brass, is aluminium which is annealed by coating the aluminium in soap and heating it up until the soap turns black and leaving to cool.

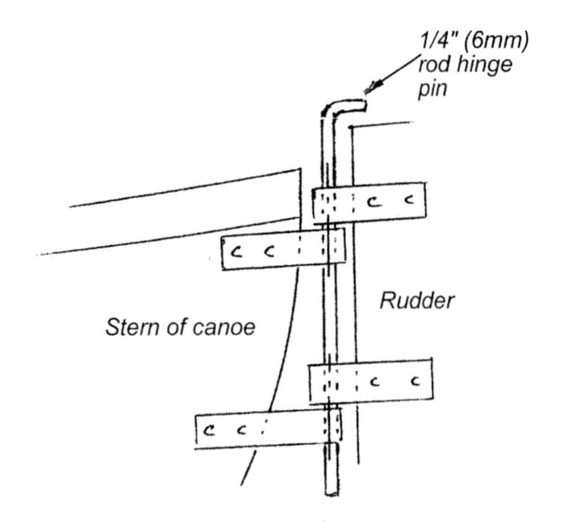

Fig 63. The pintle (pin) which forms the hinge.

The second hinge is the one that allows the rudder itself to be divided into 2 parts, the stock and the blade. The stock is the part which is hinged to the hull and which has the tiller/yoke attached to it and the blade is the lower part which actually sticks down into the water.

The blade is hinged to the stock so that when beaching the boat, the blade can flip up out of the way. A simple 6mm bolt can be used as the pivot pin for the blade (Figure 64).

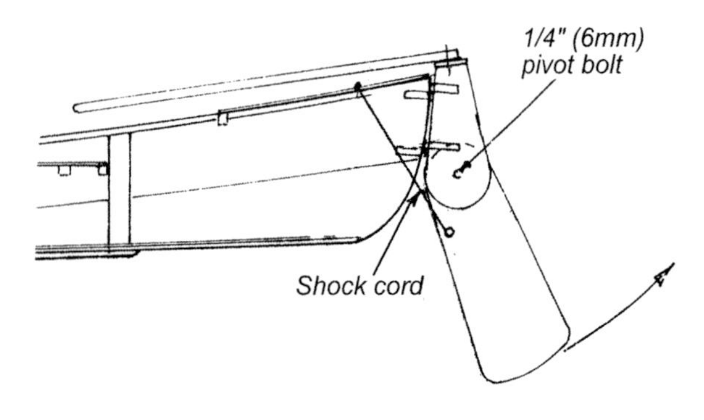

Fig 64. A pivoted rudder blade arrangement.

A rudder with pivoted blade on a Waterman 16 by Ian Davison.

The blade needs to be kept down and this is done with shock cord as shown. A cord can also be arranged so that the blade can be pulled up but this is not necessary. Both the blade and stock can be made out of plywood (9mm is better but 6mm can be used) or from aluminium.

From the rudder stock you need to be able to pass control to the cockpit and this can be done with a simple tiller or a yoke and tiller bar (Figure 65).

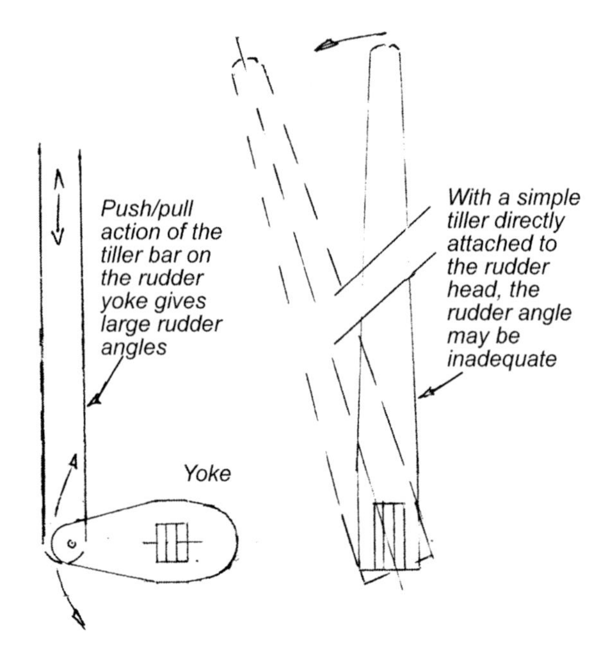

Fig 65. A yoke and push-pull tiller is better for a canoe.

A tiller, whilst being the simplest method, will only give you a small arc of turn. The yoke can be controlled either with a tiller bar using a push/pull action or by control ropes which pass forward onto peddles in the cockpit (Figure 66).

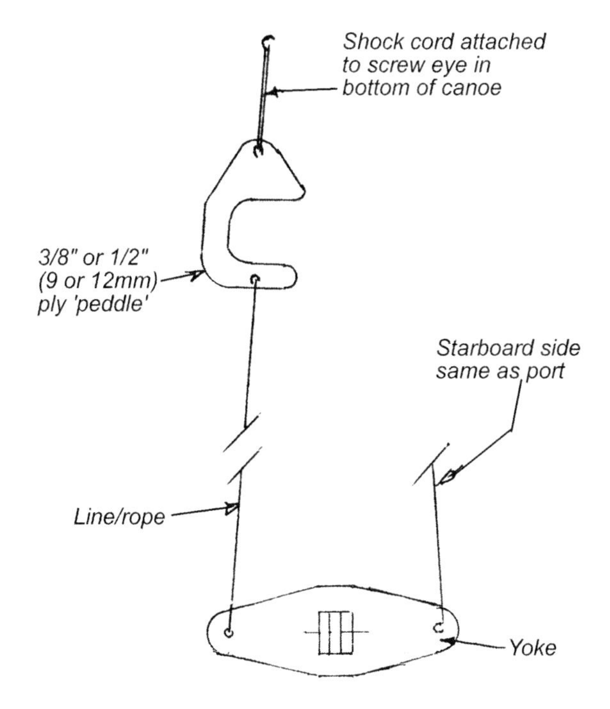

Fig 66. Foot controls for the rudder.

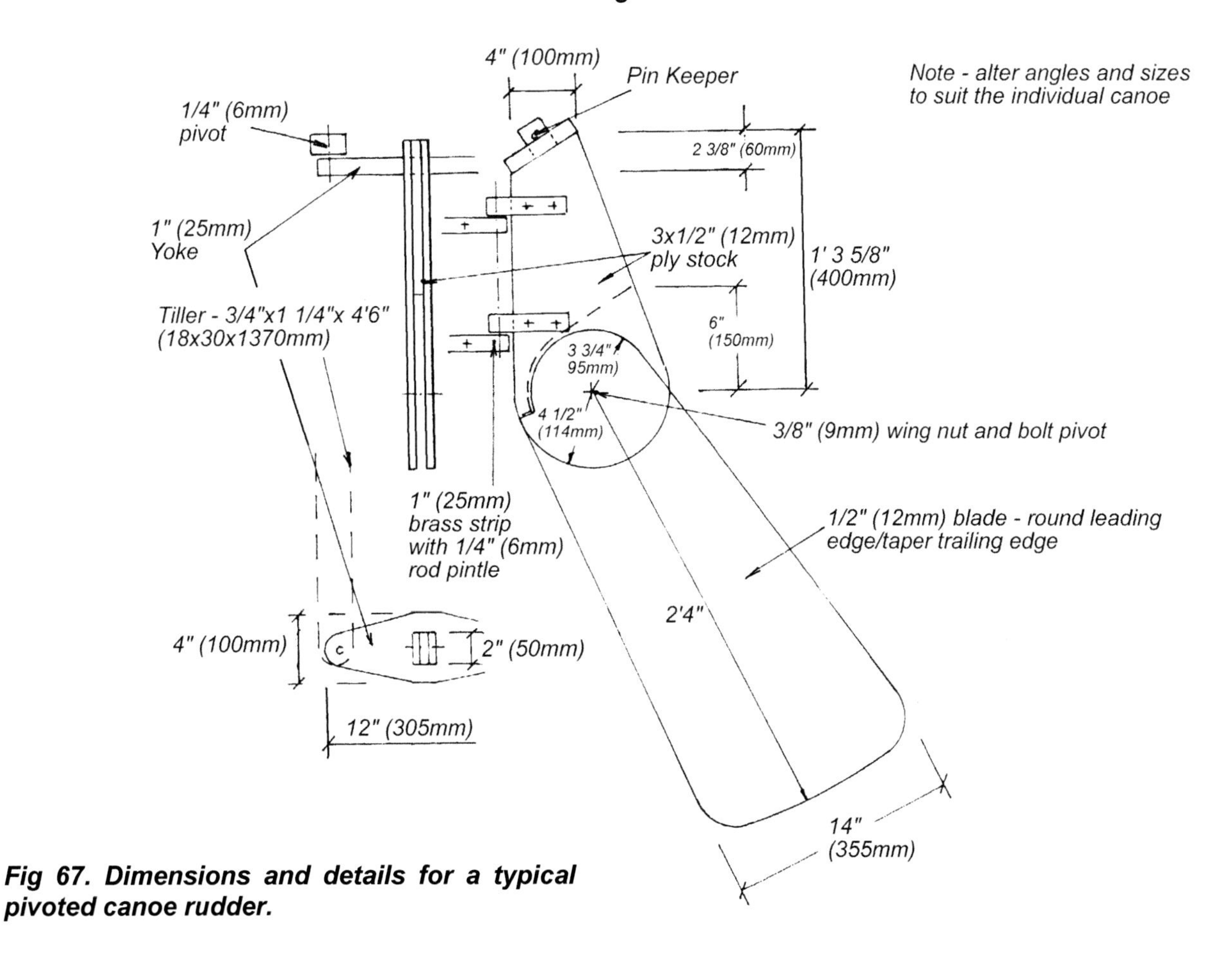

Fig 67. Dimensions and details for a typical pivoted canoe rudder.

11.3 The Keel

The keel is there to stop the canoe from going side ways and basically consists of some sort of foil section under the water which produces a force to oppose the side ways making force produced by the sails. Some of the early sailing canoes were fitted with a rather elaborate fan folding centreboard which automatically hinged out of the way when the canoe grounded. However, the only way to fit a keel onto a canoe without drastically effecting the inside of the boat, is to use some form of leeboard.

Most canoes use a simple leeboard arrangement over the side of the canoe which can be removed from the canoe when not in use. However, some sailing canoeists prefer a fixed board arrangement, usually a dagger board which is a board which works in a casing permanently fixed into the hull.

The advantage of the leeboard is that it can be removed entirely from the canoe. The daggerboard case takes up space permanently but has the advantage of being a bit more efficient and less troublesome in use than a leeboard which often has a tendency to float up and stop working.

11.3.1 The Leeboard

Rather like the rudder, there are 2 ways of deploying a leeboard the easiest way being to simply hang a plywood board over the leeward side of the canoe (the side not being hit by the wind) so that it is automatically held against the canoe side by the pressure of the canoe bearing down onto it (Figure 68).

This can be quite an effective way of doing it and simply requires a cleat on the inside of the coaming to attach the cord to. Every time you tack, you simply throw the board over

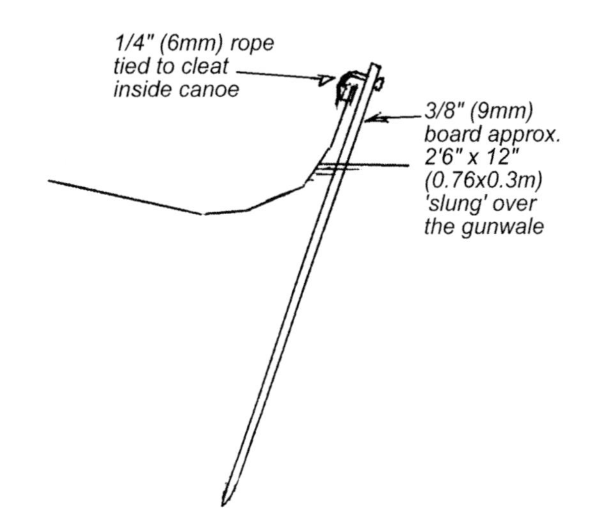

Fig 68. A simple tied leeboard.

the other side. The problem can be that the board tries to float up and simply lie on the water's surface. This can be counteracted by attaching a weight to the bottom of the board.

A method which provides easier control is to use a leeboard which is hinged to a frame or cross brace which spans the cockpit (Figure 69). The cross brace has a pair of 'L' shaped screw eyes which run from side to side in slots allowing the whole affair to be

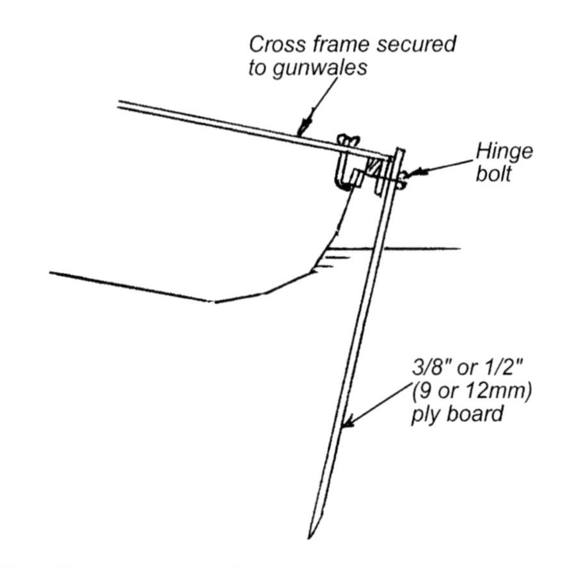

Fig 69. A leeboard fixed to a frame.

moved fore and aft along the cockpit to find the best position for the leeboard. Figure 70 gives the construction details of a typical hinged leeboard arrangement often used on canoes of around 16' (4.88m) length.

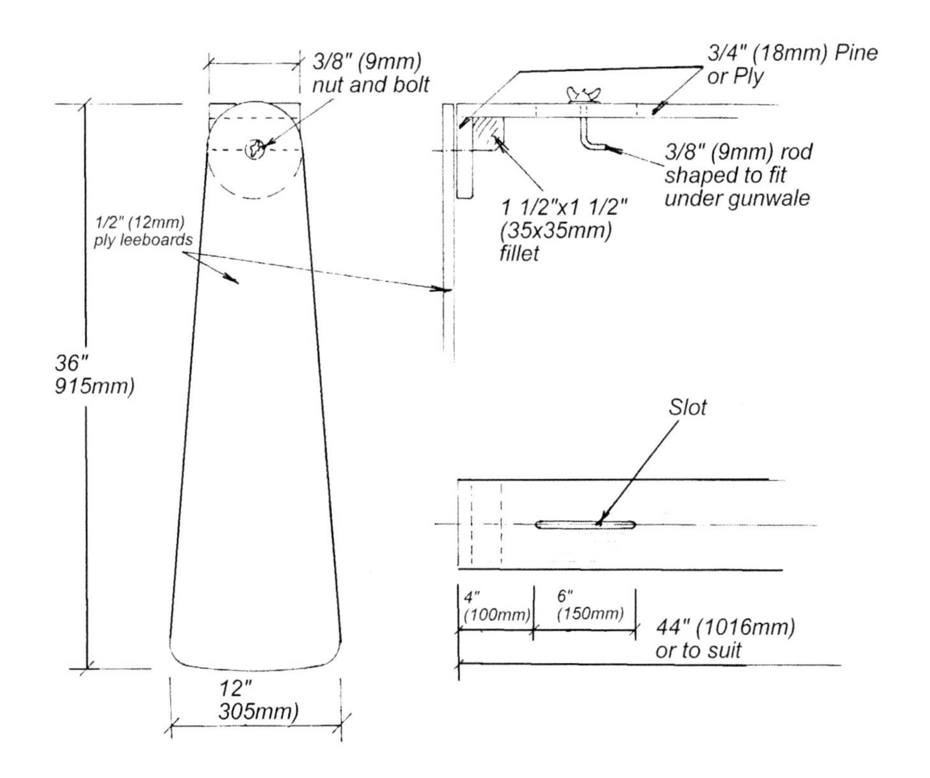

Fig 70. Construction details for a hinged leeboard.

A hinged leeboard arrangement on Brad Davis's Waterman 16.

11.3.2 The Daggerboard

Figures 71 and 72 give details of the daggerboard arrangement sometimes fitted to our Beaver canoe design. It has also been used on several other canoes and works well. The daggerboard is housed in a case which is fixed into the hull with both it's top and bottom ends open so that the board can be slotted into it to pass out through the bottom of the canoe. Unlike the leeboard (or a pivoted centreboard on larger craft), the board does not pivot up when you hit the river bottom which usually brings your sailing to an abrupt halt. I do not usually consider using a centreboard, which is a pivoted board working in a longer case, because the case usually takes up too much space in the canoe.

The inside surfaces of the case need to be well coated with epoxy before assembly and the case must be well fixed into the hull and adequately supported with knees and attachment to seats etc.

A daggerboard case on a Waterman 16 by Ian Davison.

1/2" (12mm) doublers
2 1/2" (64mm)
3'4" (1016mm)
1/2" (12mm) ply dagger-board - round edges
2" 50mm)
12" (305mm)
Head 9' (2743mm)
Leech 11'1" (3378mm)
Diag 6' 1 1/2" (1867mm)
Luff 2'10" (864mm)
Foot 6'4" (1930mm)
Ply knee epoxied to hull

Fig 71. The daggerboard arrangement on a Selway Fisher Beaver design.

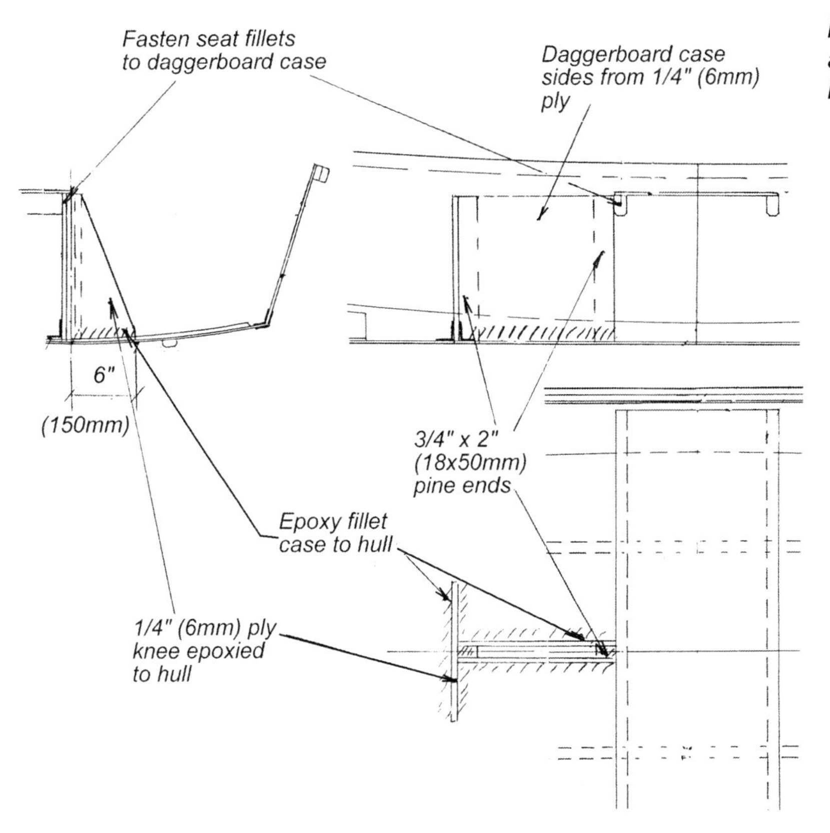

Fig 72. The daggerboard case arrangement on a Selway Fisher Beaver design.

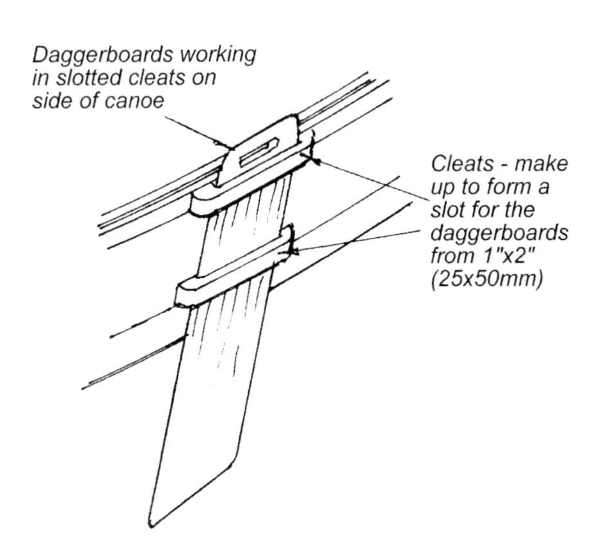

Fig 73. The daggeboard mounted on the side of the canoe hull as a leeboard—the cleats are 'U' shaped pieces of wood—a strip of timber with a piece removed from the middle of one side so that when screwed to the hull side, a slot is left for the daggerboard.

Figure 73 shows an alternative arrangement for mounting the daggerboard on the side of the hull as a leeboard. In this case two wood cleats are made up and secured to the side of the canoe leaving a slot in which the board goes up and down. The top of the board usually has a handle formed and is thickened so that it does not slide right down and out of the cleats.

The two cleats need to be well spaced and therefore this arrangement is best suited to fairly slab sided single chine hulls where the cleats can be at least 12" (305mm) apart. The arrangement is often only fitted to one side using just one daggerboard. If it is fitted to both sides, two boards can be used with their outer surfaces flat and an aerofoil shape on their inboard faces only but this is more than is usually required for canoe sailing.

11.4 The Balance between Rig & Hull

Where should the sail plan and leeboards be sited on the canoe for maximum sailing efficiency? Well, going into a long description on the aero/hydrodynamic balance of a sail boat would take a whole book by itself and really we want to add a sailing rig to the canoe in the quickest and easiest way, so I shall simply mention a few helpful pointers.

To start with, the mast is usually positioned close to the forward end of the canoe cockpit for a normal kayak type canoe or about 1/3 rd of the boat's length from the bow. This keeps the mast out of the way and lets the rope controlling the setting of the sail (the sheet) fall directly to hand at the aft end of the cockpit.

Having settled on a position for the mast, we now need to position the leeboard so that there is 'balance' between the rig and leeboard. What is balance? Well, in very basic terms, a rig which is balanced with the leeboard is one which allows the canoe to sail well to windward with the helm (tiller) more or less positioned amidships. If the rig is too far forward in relation to the position of the leeboard then the force and moment acting will tend to push the boat's bow off to leeward which will require you to push the helm down to leeward (the opposite side to the side being hit by the wind) to counteract it. This is called 'lee helm' (Figure 74).

The opposite will happen if the rig is too far aft. This produces 'weather helm' with the tiller having to be pulled up to windward. Most sailors like just a little 'weather helm' to give a positive feel to the steering (Figure 75).

How do you get the correct balance? From

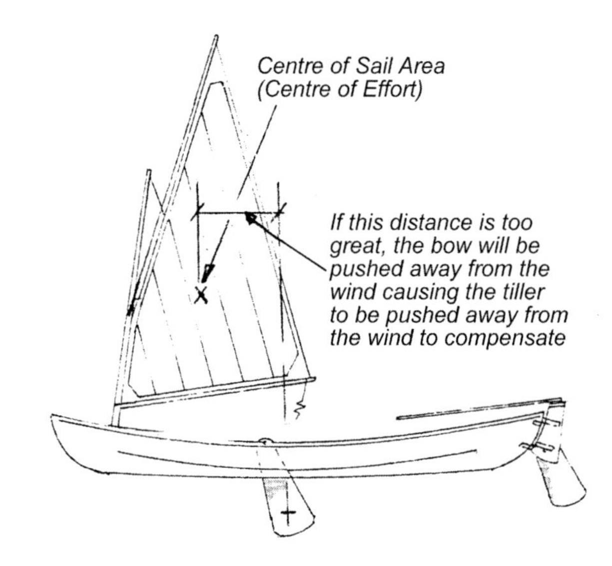

Fig 74. Sail too far forward for correct 'balance'.

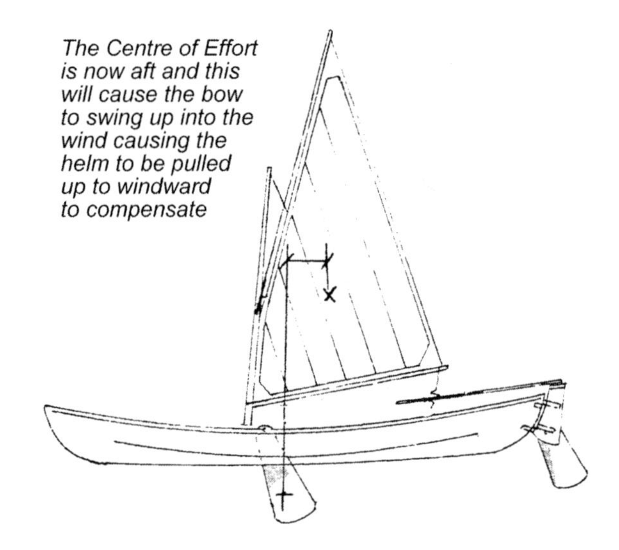

Fig 75. Sail too far aft for correct 'balance'.

our experience, the correct balance most often occurs in canoes and small boats when the leeboard is positioned directly below the Centre of Effort of the sail plan (Figure 76).

This varies a bit depending on the type and cut of the sails but is generally true. The Centre of Effort is simply taken to be the centre of area of the sail plan. To find this, you find the centre of area of each sail and

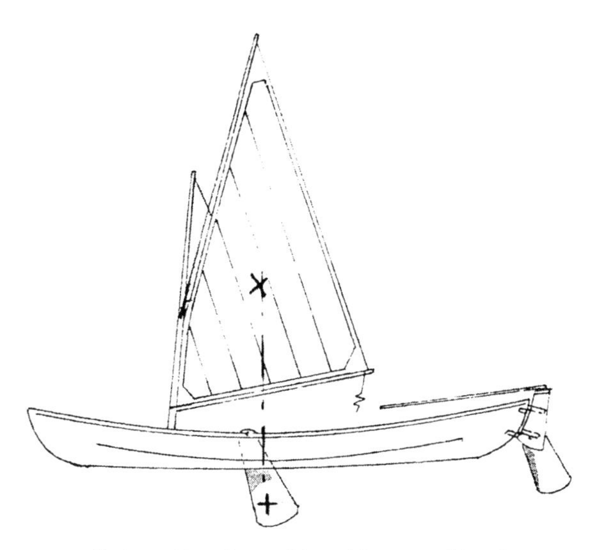

'Balance' is often achieved in a small boat (canoes and dinghies) when the Centre of Effort (Area) is in-line with the centre of the leeboard

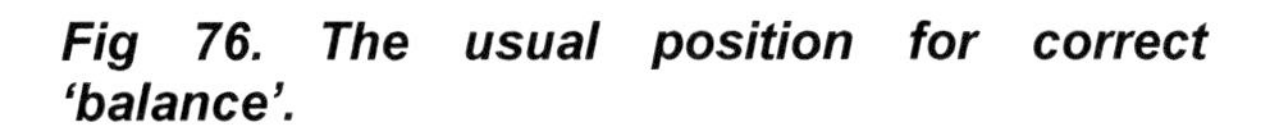

Fig 76. The usual position for correct 'balance'.

then if you have more than one sail, combine the centres. Easy?! Well yes it is, once you understand how to find the centre of area of a 2 dimensional shape and to help you we have included Figure 77 which gives a step by step procedure for doing this.

At the end of the day, experimenting by moving the leeboard position fore and aft is often the best way to do it.

Above—a bat's wind rig on the 5050 sailing canoe.

Above—Marcello Ferrero's Beaver fitted with floats and a lateen rig.

Below—the Bermudan sail rig on the JC10.

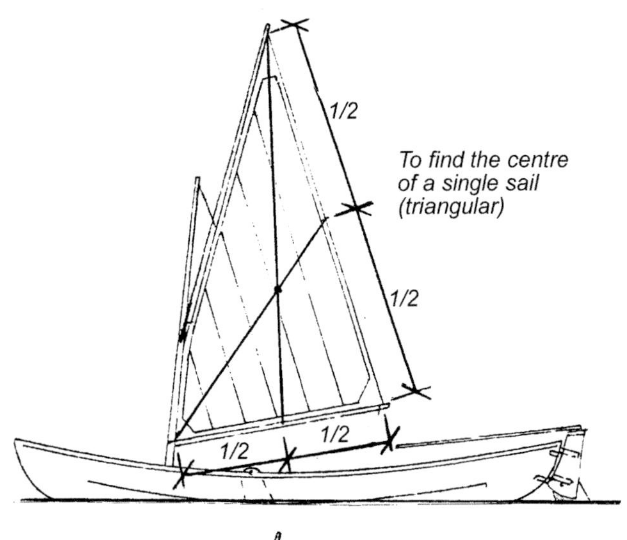

Fig 77. Finding the Centre of Effort of the sail plan.

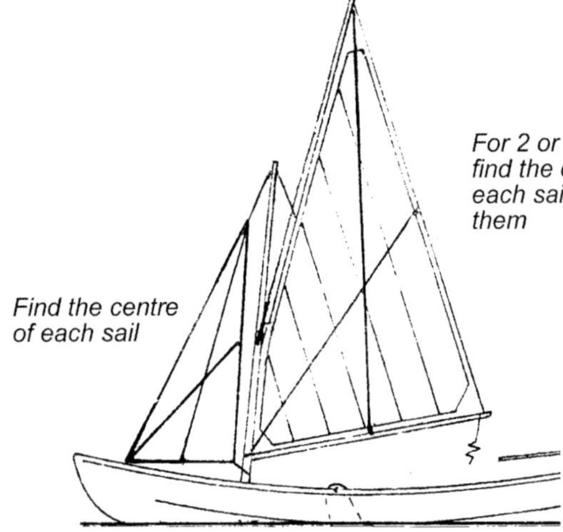

and then......

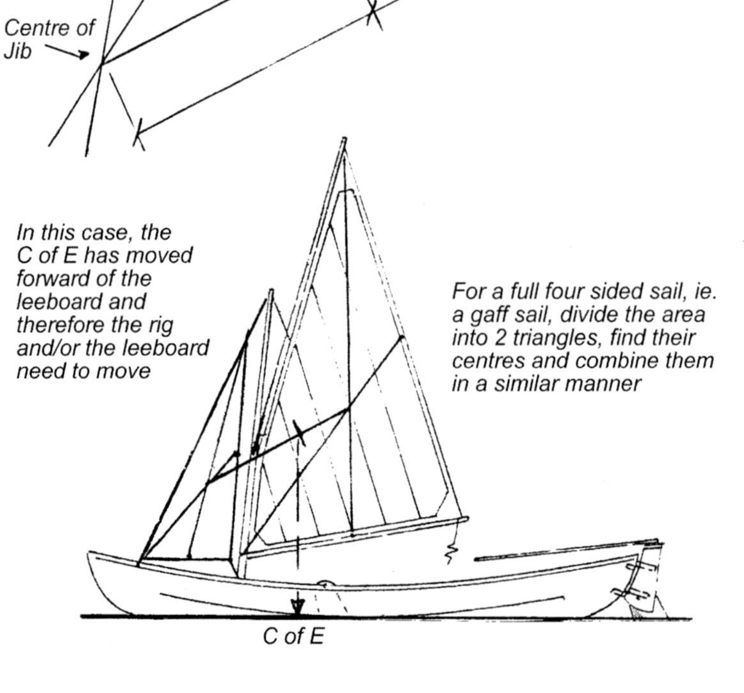

A well balanced double lug (or lug yawl) rig on a Beaver design.

11.5 The Sails & Spars

11.5.1 The Mast Support (Step)

It is better if the rig is kept simple with spars short enough to fit easily inside the canoe. The rig should be light in weight with as few strings as possible, so cutting out the standing rigging which is used to hold the mast up, is a good idea. Instead, step the mast through a hole in a cross brace with the mast step on the hog of the canoe (Figure 78).

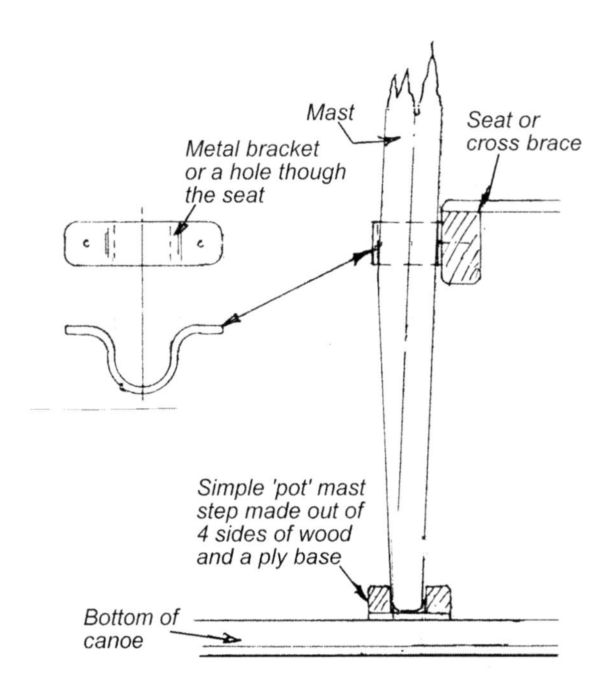

Fig 78. A simple mast step arrangement.

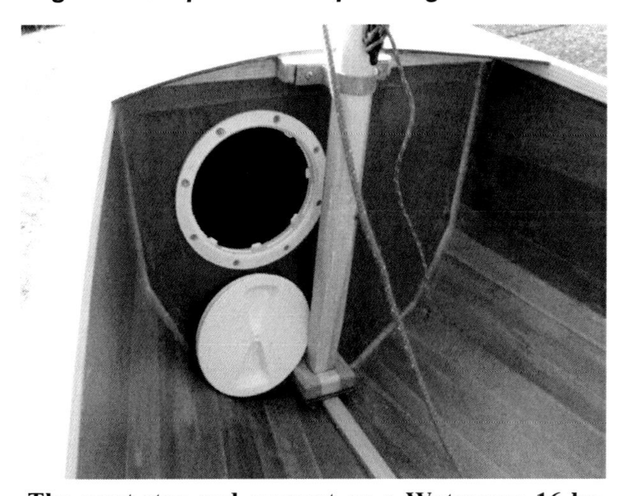

The mast step and support on a Waterman 16 by Ian Davison.

11.5.2 Suitable Rigs

The type of sailing rig that you use comes down to personal preference but in case you have little experience in these matters I will offer a few pointers here.

Keep the rig low in shape to keep the boat stable. From this point of view, cutting the sail area into two sails is better than putting the area into one sail only. On the other hand having two sails means that there are more strings to control. Another important consideration is the actual amount of sail area to go for. For most double canoes, a total area of around 3 sq.mtrs (approx.30 sq.ft.) seems best. This area will move you along nicely without becoming too much of a handful. The three rigs that I have successfully used are the gunter rig both with and without a jib (Figure 79), the lateen rig (Figure 80) which is very easy to put up, uses a shorter mast but perhaps is not as efficient as the gunter rig which comes closer to the Bermudan rig of larger modern craft—and finally the lug rig which is a simple but powerful sail type (Figure 81).

Fig 79. The Gunter Rig.

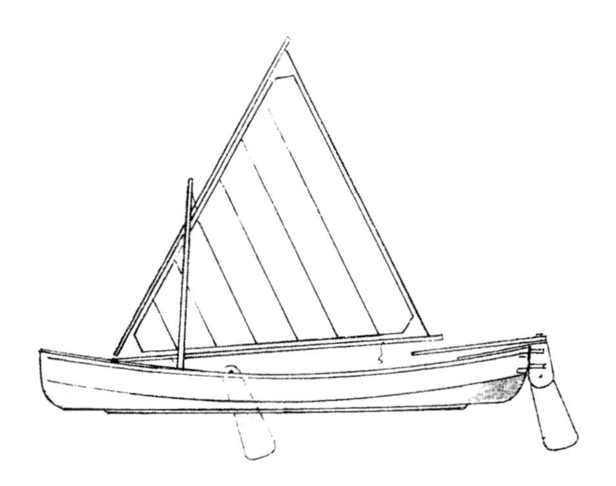

Fig 80. The Lateen Rig.

Figure 81 shows a simple double sail arrangement (lug yawl) used on the Beaver design.

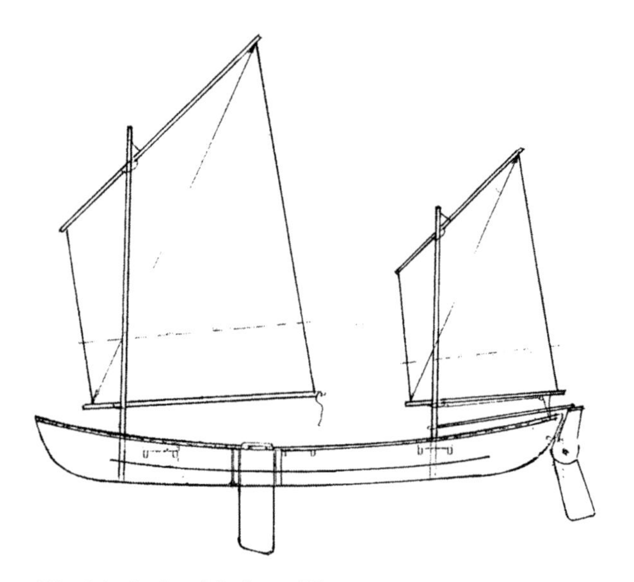

Fig 81. A double Lug Rig.

Spars (the mast etc.) can be nothing more than simple broom sticks although these can be too thick at times. The mast is often around 1 1/2" (35mm) diameter at the base and tapered to just 3/4" (18mm) at the top. The boom and gaff can be 1 1/8" (28mm) diameter. Ordinary White Pine is fine although Spruce is lighter. I have also used bamboo which is hollow and therefore light in weight and very stiff although impossible to glue too.

Sails are made from the lightest Terylene or Nylon cloth and simply tied to the spars or made with sleeves into which the spars fit (Figure 82). There is no need to get too technical about the construction of the sails. If you read any books on the subject, you will see that for larger sails, the sail shape is divided up into panels and that the seams are specially tapered to give the correct aerofoil shape to the sail.

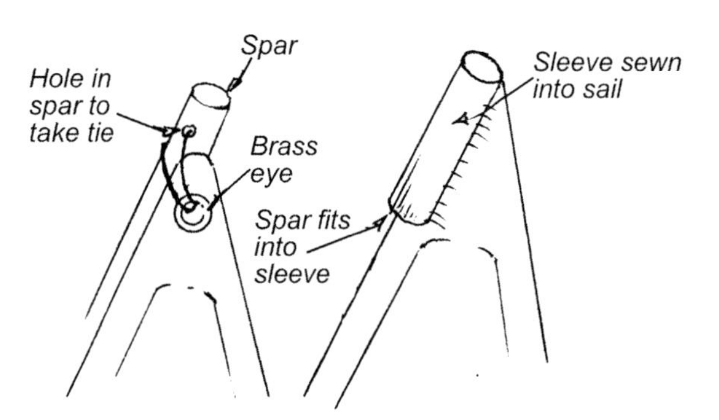

Fig 82. Attaching the sails to the spars.

For a canoe, and especially if you are only going to use the sail when the wind is in the right direction, the right aerofoil shape for the sail can be induced into the middle of the sail by cutting and stitching the sides of the sail with curves rather than with straight lines. If you look at Figure 83 you will see that when the sail is stretched along a spar, the material in the curve that has been cut into the edge of the sail has to go somewhere and it actually goes into the body of the sail thereby inducing shape into it.

There is no need to stretch the sail too tight along the spar and if the maximum depth of the curve cut into the edge of the sail is closer to one end of the side, the induced shape will

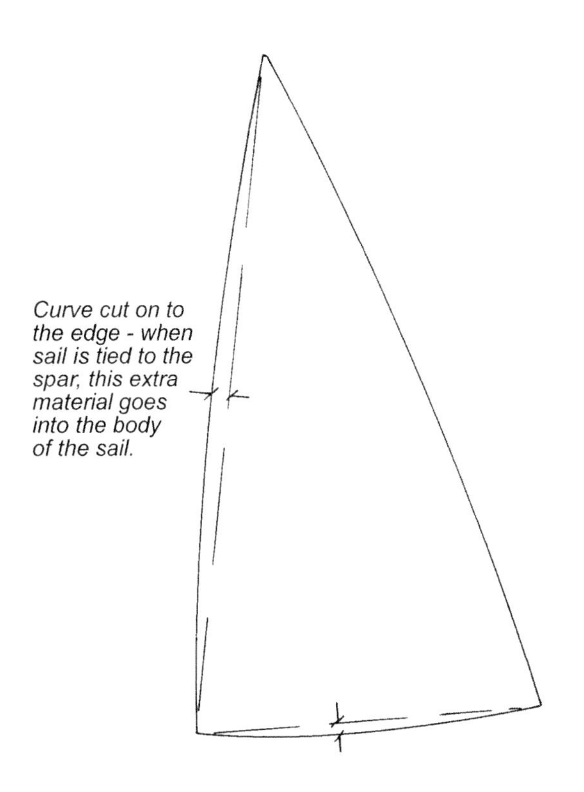

Fig 83. The curves worked into the edges of the sail.

be greater towards that end. By doing this, we can end up with a good aerodynamic shape and Figure 84 gives the typical dimensions for the curved edges of a gunter main and jib. Similar curves would be used on the edges of a lateen sail.

As far as stitching the edges is concerned, this has to be done in order to prevent fraying and is best carried out as shown in Figure 85 with a reasonable width of seam and 2 lines of stitching. An ordinary domestic sewing machine can be used to do the stitching. For this size of sail, there is often no need to sew strengthening patches into the corners of the sail and a simple eyelet kit (from hardware and craft shops) can be used to make the holes for attaching the sail to the spars.

Draw the shape of the sail down onto a floor, cut the cloths to suit leaving 2" overlaps at the edges. Sew the cloths together preferably

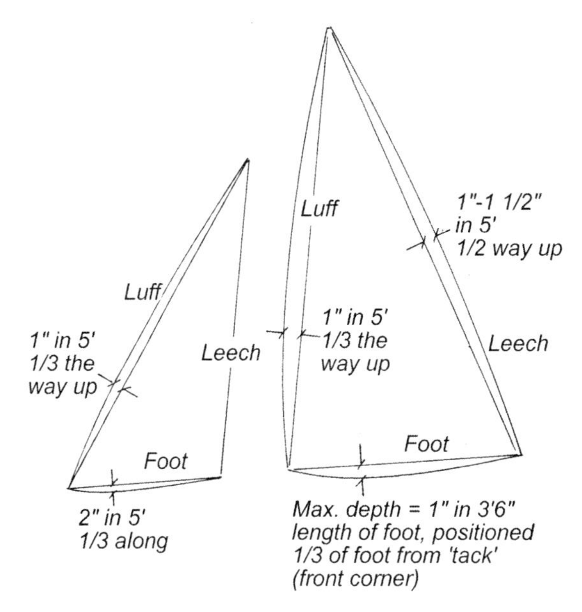

Fig 84. The position for the curves and their size.

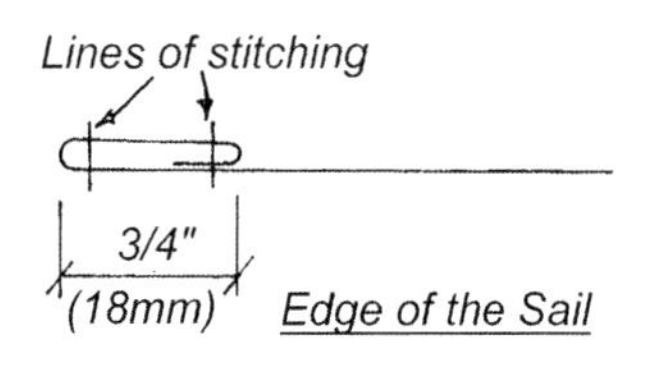

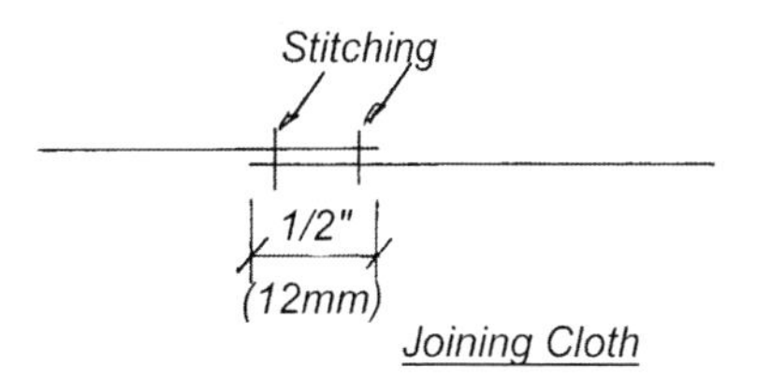

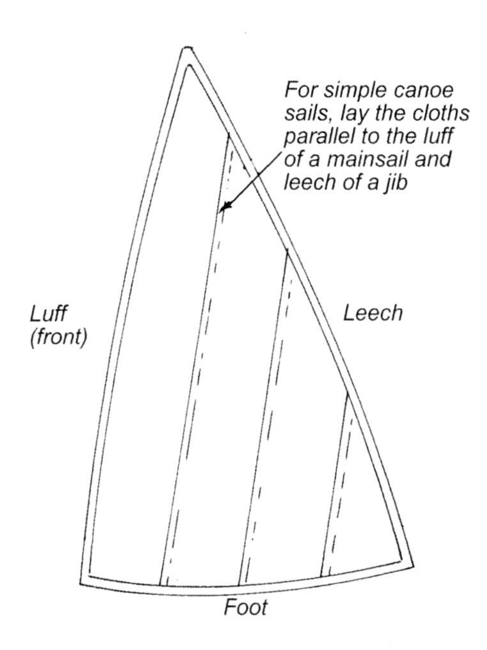

Fig 85. Sewing the sails together.

using a zig-zag stitch, mark the shape of the sail onto the cloth and finish the edge as shown by folding the edge over and sewing the outer line of stitching first. Use tape to hold the cloths together whilst sewing.

Some sailing canoeists just want a simple rig which can be raised to catch the wind from behind them and dropped when they turn a bend in the river and the wind is no longer coming from behind them. This arrangement allows the wind to be used to help alleviate the paddling but without the need for more complicated fore and aft rigs which the more serious sailing canoeist might use. Figure 86 shows a simple set-up where the mast can hinge back when not in use and then be quickly raised by pulling on the running forestay. The heel of the mast comes up against a stop preventing it from hinging forward.

All the ropes should be led aft to be in easy reach of the crew. The sheets can be in a continuous loop and could be led through small eyes mounted on the gunwale for convenience and the mast step could be more easily made from bent 4mm aluminium or brass sheet.

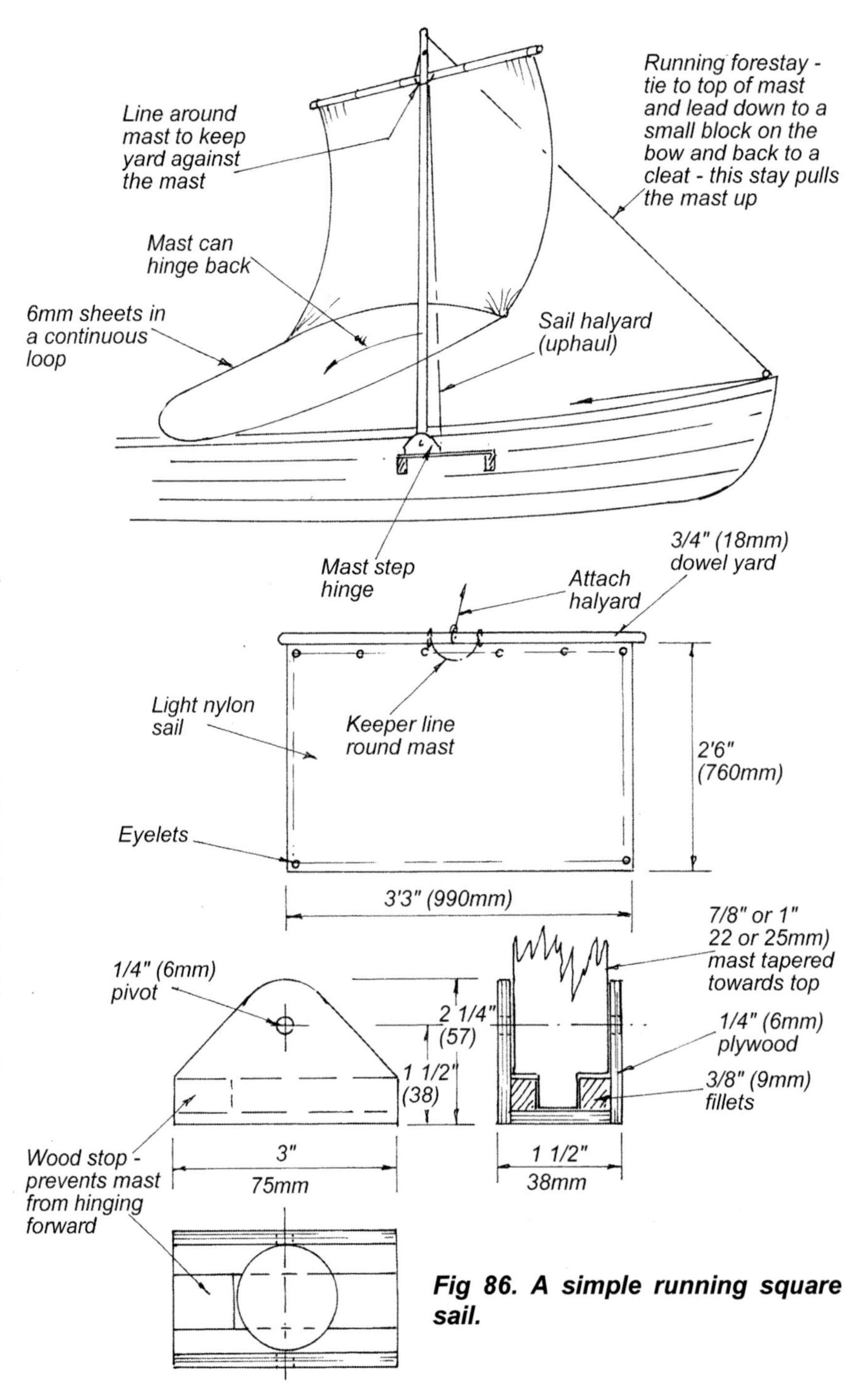

Fig 86. A simple running square sail.

Chapter 12

CANOE EQUIPMENT

12.1 Rudders

Apart from the need for a rudder when sailing, rudders can also help when paddling. In an open canoe, a rudder can help keep a straight course when you are paddling on one side and a rudder can reduce the effort in turning a kayak.

12.1.1 Kayak Rudders

Kayak rudders want to produce as little additional drag as possible and can be quite small in area. They are usually high aspect in shape with a long slim blade which should be shaped carefully. Figures 87 and 88 shows a typical arrangement with a ply blade which slides up and down in a hollow box ply stock. If the blade lies back or is vertical in position, a thin wire is sometimes used going from the bottom of the blade to the hull to prevent a build up of weed etc. If the blade slopes the other way with it's lower tip aft of the top, this is not always necessary.

Figure 89 shows a hinged arrangement which some canoeists prefer.

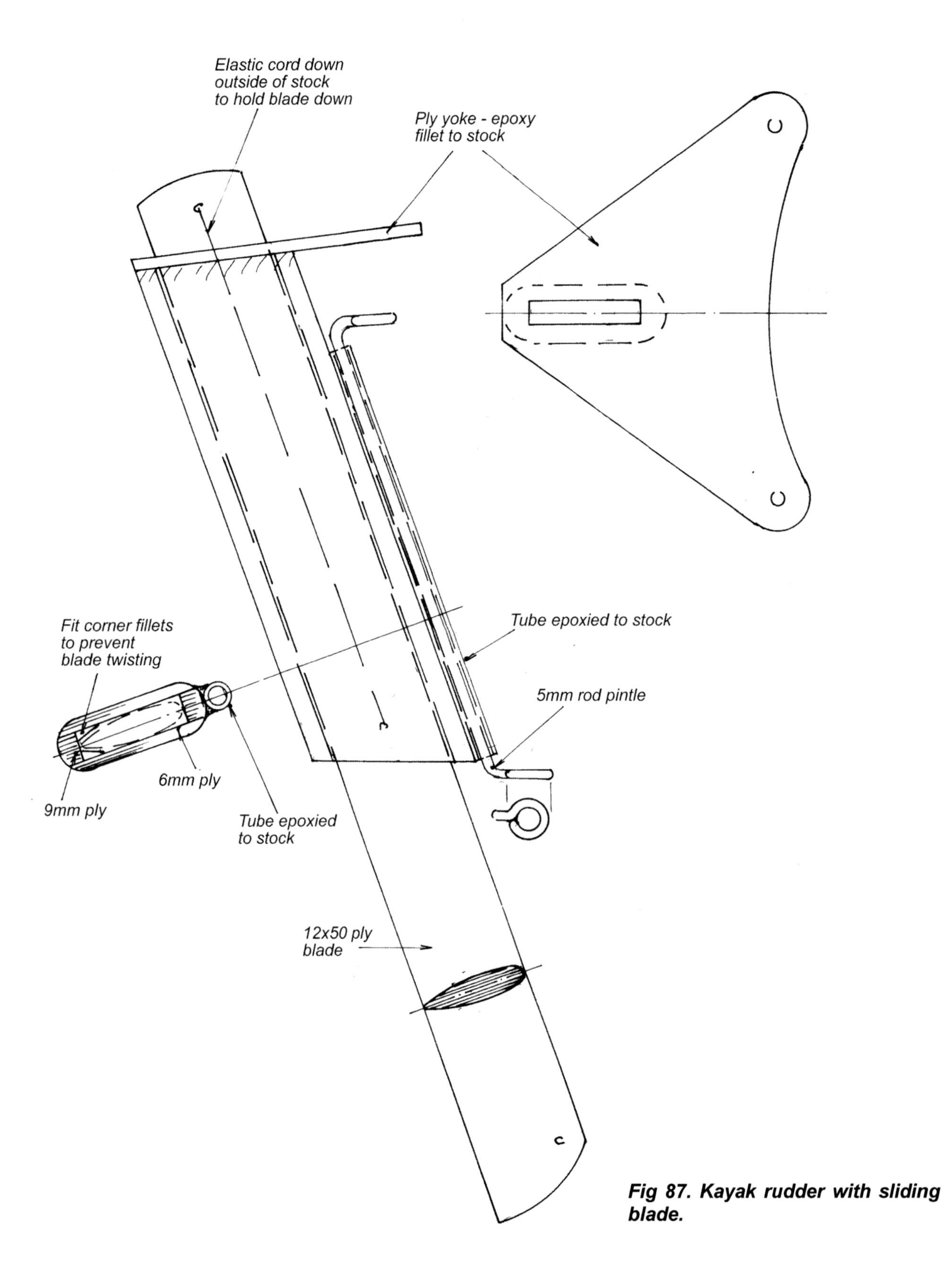

Fig 87. Kayak rudder with sliding blade.

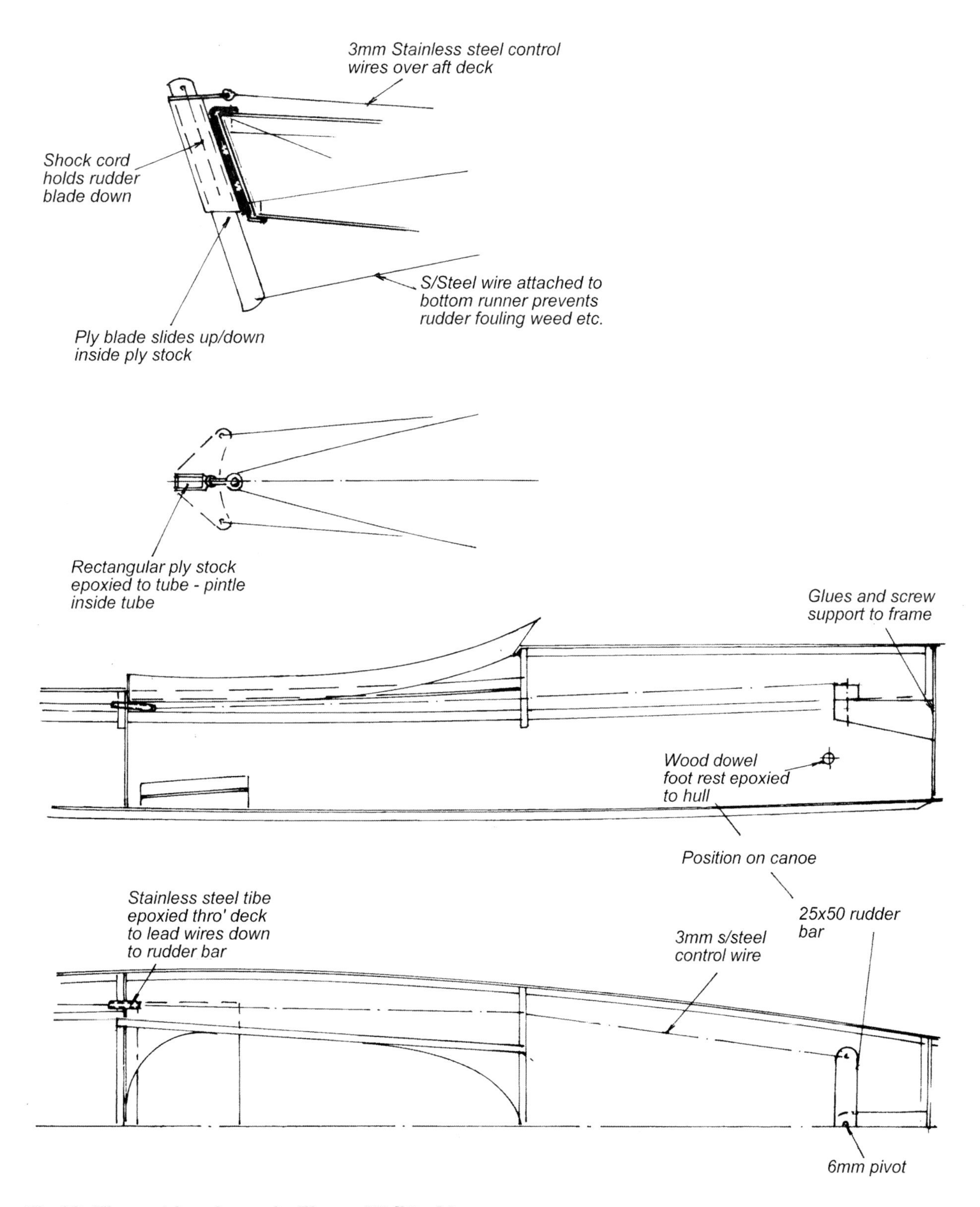

Fig 88. The rudder shown in Figure 87 fitted to a kayak.

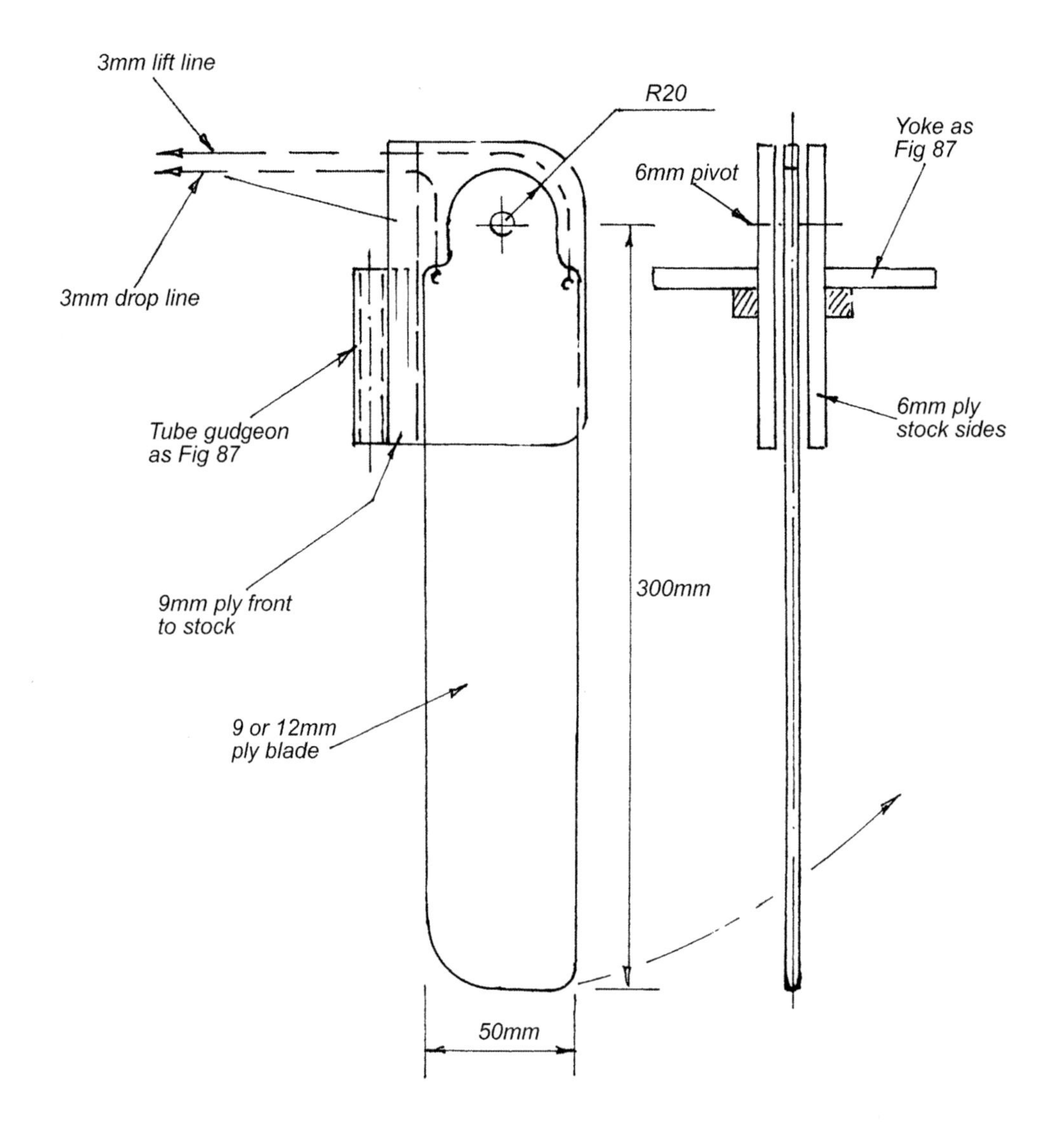

Fig 89. A hinged kayak rudder.

This hinged arrangement may use 3mm aluminium for the blade. Make the stock wide enough to take the drop and lift lines attached to the blade. The neatest way to attach them is to loop the lines through their respective holes and then to use thin binding twine to bind the end to the line.

12.1.2 More Open Canoe Rudders

See Figure 67 for a standard open canoe rudder with a hinged blade. This is a very efficient design but you may not want to go to the trouble of a hinged arrangement.

To have sufficient rudder blade area, rudders with a fixed blade would need to be deeper than the hull which would cause problems in shallow water. One way around this problem is to use a low aspect ration type rudder with a wide and shallow blade with a 'fence' on the bottom edge.

When the rudder is used by turning it, hydrodynamic forces occur which produce a 'high' pressure on one side and a 'low' pressure on the opposite side. The fence stops the 'high' pressure side of the blade escaping to the 'low' pressure side and increases the efficiency of the blade.

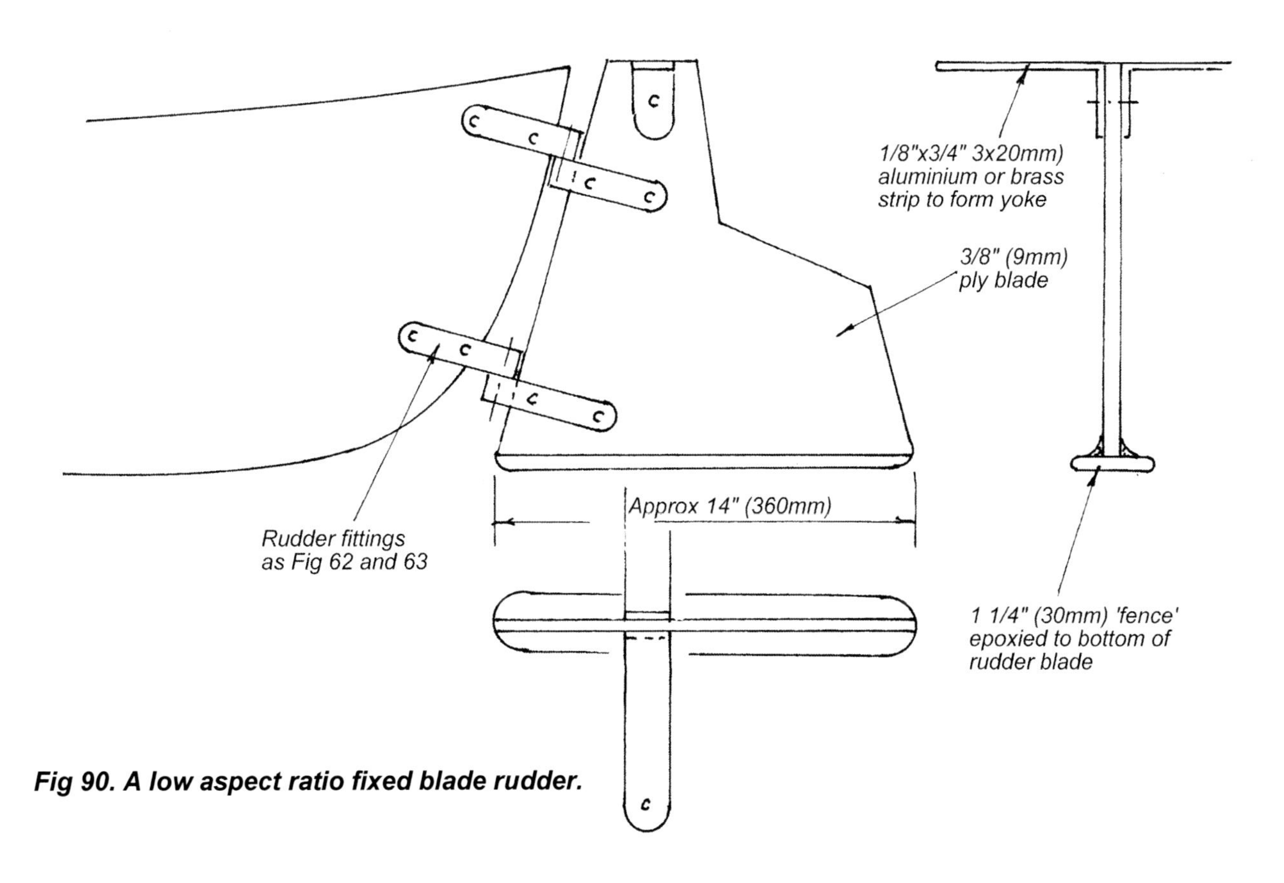

Fig 90. A low aspect ratio fixed blade rudder.

12.2 Making the Canoe in Two Halves

It is often an advantage to either build or store a canoe in two or more parts. Many of the Selway Fisher canoe plans are symmetrical about the midship line and can therefore be easily split in the centre of the hull. Furthermore, the plank shapes are usually given with their join at this midships (centre) point.

This means that the canoe can be made in two halves and all that is needed is a bulkhead fitted to each half which can be bolted through to connect the two halves together.

The arrangement shown in Figure 91 shows the plywood bulkheads connected to the ply hull sides using a 1"x2" (25x50mm) wood fillet frame. The parts for this frame can be half-checked together before being glued and nailed to the bulkheads.

To strengthen the corner between the bulkhead and the hull sides I usually use a triangular knee glued and screwed to the top of the bulkhead and sides.

The two halves are fixed together with six well distributed 1/4" (6mm) bolts or machine screws fitted with large penny washers under the heads and nuts. There is no need for any washer/gasket material between the two canoe halves—I did at one time fit a neoprene sheet washer between the two halves but found this unnecessary. In fact I have lowered the top of the bulkheads so that I could fit a seat over them and still found that water did not get in.

Above—a Fisher Prospector being built in two halves showing the plywood bulkhead at the centre joining point.

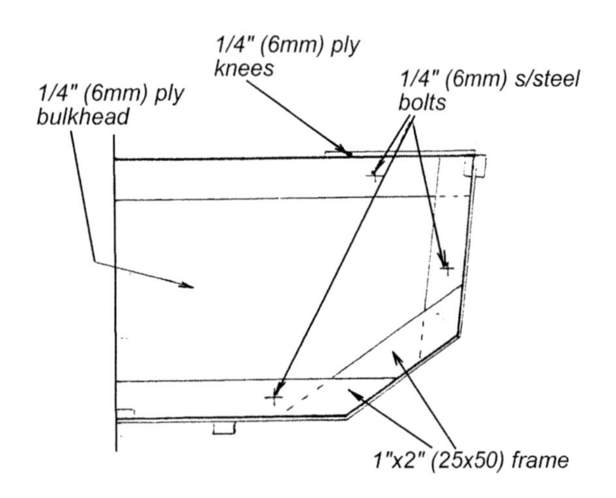

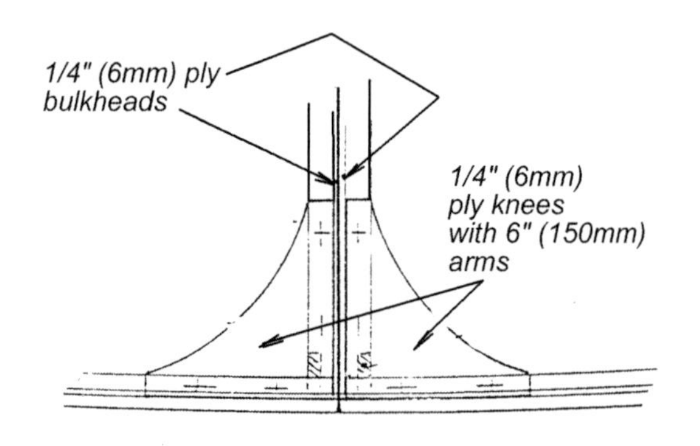

Fig 91. Joining the hull in two halves.

12.3 Sponsons

Sometimes a little more stability is required because you are using a relatively narrow canoe in rough conditions or when trying to teach youngsters to canoe. Floats, separated from the hull are not always convenient and the stability can be increased significantly by using simple sponsons.

These may be plastic tubes, which can be obtained from most builder's merchants with suitable end caps, fixed to the sides of the canoe. For a typical 16' (4.88m) canoe, tubes 5' to 6' (1.5-1.8m) long are required with a diameter of 6"-8" (150-200mm). Figure 92 shows a simple set up with wood frames/ beams used to hold the tubes securely to the sides of the canoe.

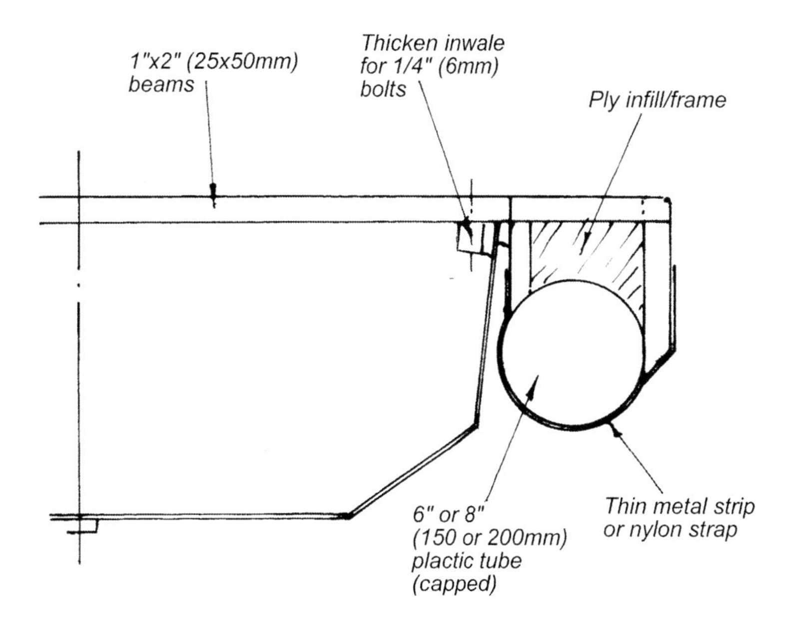

Fig 92. Simple plastic tube sponsons.

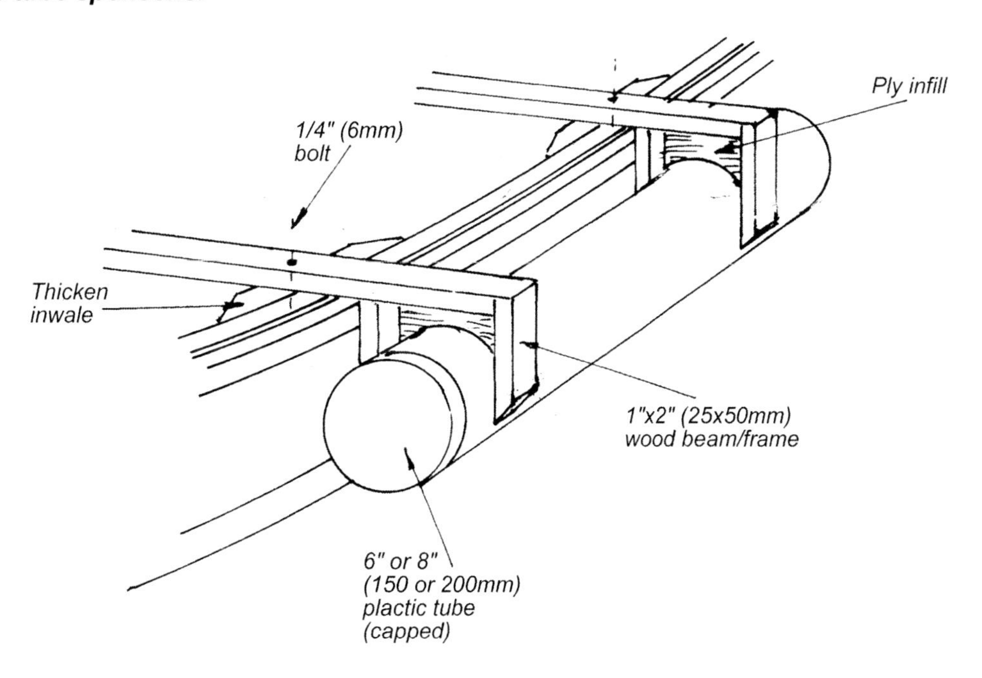

12.4 Floats

Proper floats (or Amas) turn a simple canoe into a different craft altogether. Larger sailing rigs can be used, higher loads can be carried and more crew accommodated.

The floats want to be easy to fit so that the canoe can easily be changed back for it's original use.

In most situations, just one float can be fitted on one side of the canoe but there is no reason why two floats cannot be used to form a simple trimaran.

The beams may be of simple dowel or broom stick and fitted to the gunwales with heavy duty pipe clips screwed into the structure below—the width between the float and the hull may be adjusted but the total beam would normally be around 6' to 7' (1.8-2.1m).

To prevent the beams from coming out of the pipe clips during use simply put a screw into the beam either side of the clip (to be removed when the float is disassembled).

Figure 93 gives the details for a simple float used on the Selway Fisher Ranger design—it has also been used on canoes like the Fisher Prospector.

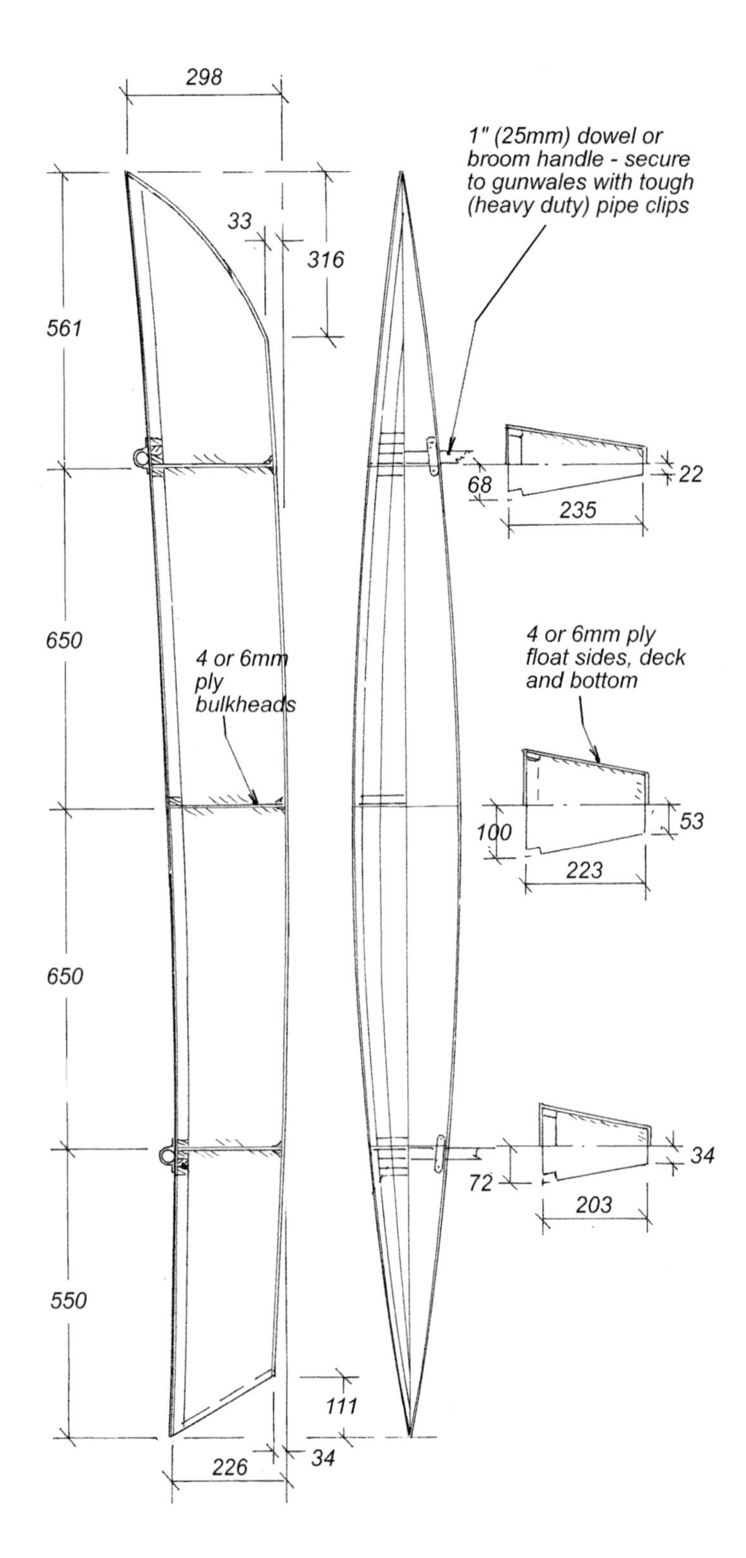

Fig 93. The float design used on the Ranger canoe and which has been used on several other Selway Fisher Designs.

Above—Steve Cullis' Fisher Prospector fitted with Ranger floats—note how the beams are simply tied down into the hull.

Below—A 18' Waka Ama in New Zealand showing a float/Ama arrangement fitted to one side only—the beams are simply tied in position.

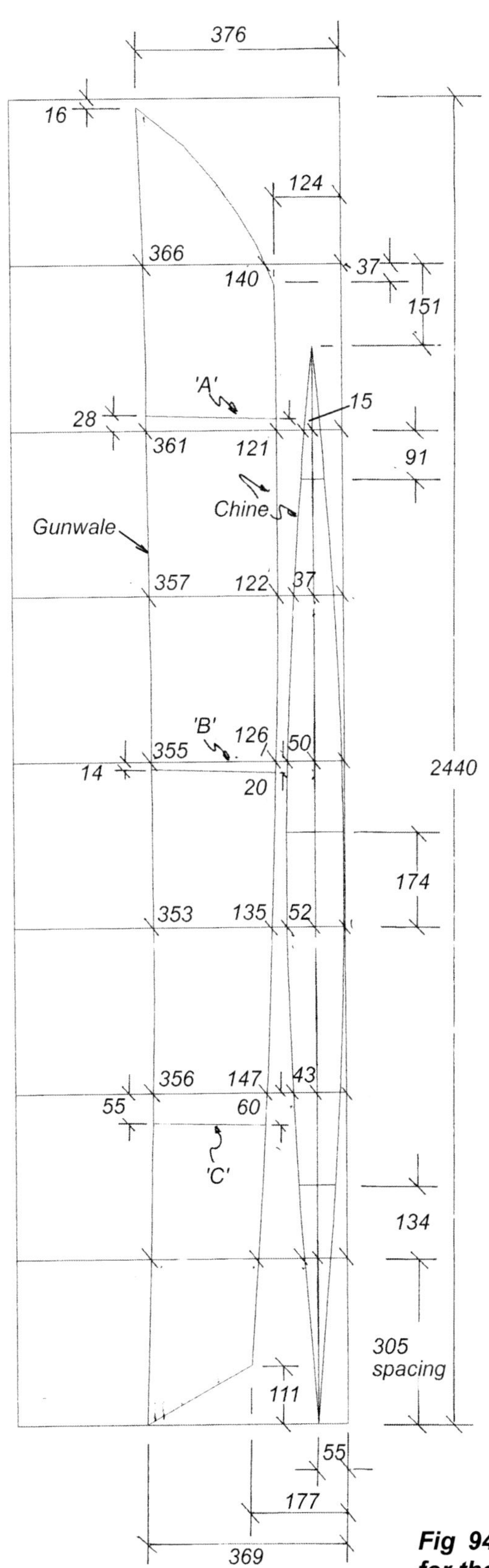

Fig 94. The hull panel and bulkhead shapes for the Ranger float.

12.5 Outboard Brackets & Wells

Many years ago, whilst a lad messing about on the Thames at Reading I witnessed the rather interesting attempts to motorize a fibreglass kayak with an outboard motor. There were problems, not least because, on a kayak, with a long aft deck, the helmsman could not sit close to the outboard in order to control it and the trim of the kayak, of course, with a heavy outboard clamped to the aft end was very much bow up!

I have written in detail about the results of this experiment elsewhere but let us just say that they were very wet!

I use this incident to illustrate a couple of points—the first is that, on a lightweight boat with a high length to beam ratio, a heavy outboard mounted right aft is not a good idea from the point of view of trim, unless you can offset the load with weight at the forward end of the canoe. Second, too much power will cause problems by over-powering the canoe making steering difficult. Third, good control is essential and if this means that you have to sit beside the outboard causing more problems with trim, this needs to be catered for.

Do not, unless you are building an outboard motor canoe which has a proper transom and wide sections aft to take the weight, try to fit the sort of outboard you would fit to the same length of dinghy or dayboat.

Most 14'-18' (4.3-5.5m) canoe need only a small lightweight outboard no more than 1/2—1 1/2 hp to move them well. Ideally a small electric outboard would be fine with the battery mounted as close to the middle of the canoe as possible.

The pointed aft end of most canoes means that it is difficult to mount an outboard directly over the stern—there are some fairly complicated brackets which do allow this, but I have found the neatest and least complicated solution is to hang the outboard off to one side (Figure 95).

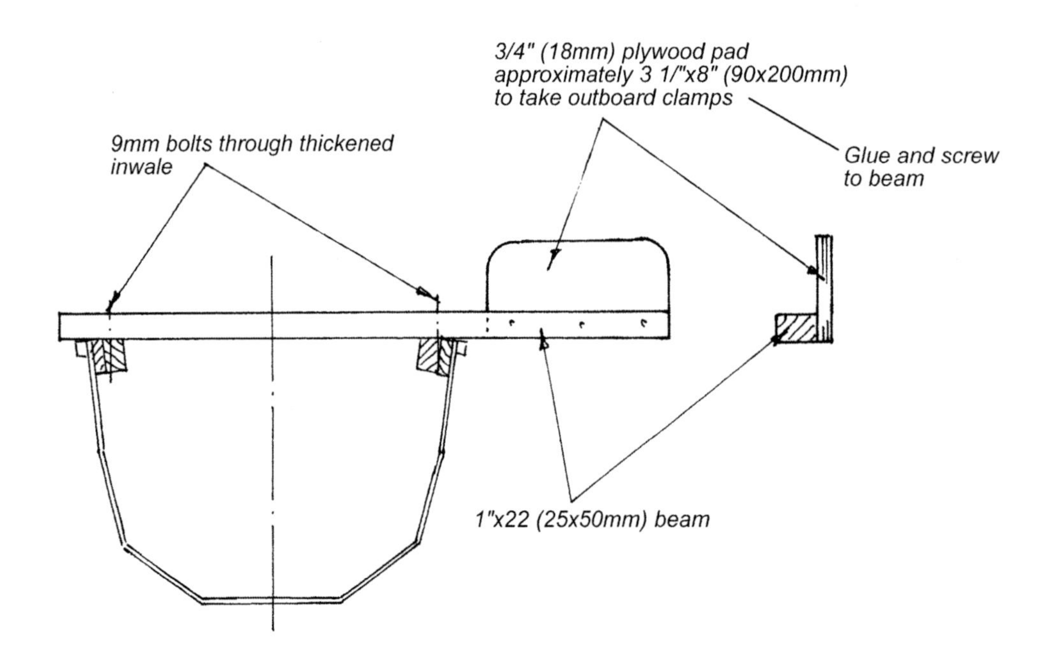

Fig 95. A simple offset outboard bracket.

I have seen this arrangement used with the outboard beam mounted close to the middle of the canoe, which overcomes the problem of longitudinal trim. However, steering the canoe with the outboard can be difficult with the outboard mounted so far forward—the canoe tends to slew to one side and pivot strangely rather than turn in a graceful arc.

I have shown bolts to secure the beam to the gunwales of the canoe but a quicker clamping system can be used perhaps like that shown in Figure 65 for the leeboard, but make sure whatever system you use, it is full proof—the last thing you want is for the outboard to disappear below the water!

Outboards mounted on brackets are fine for

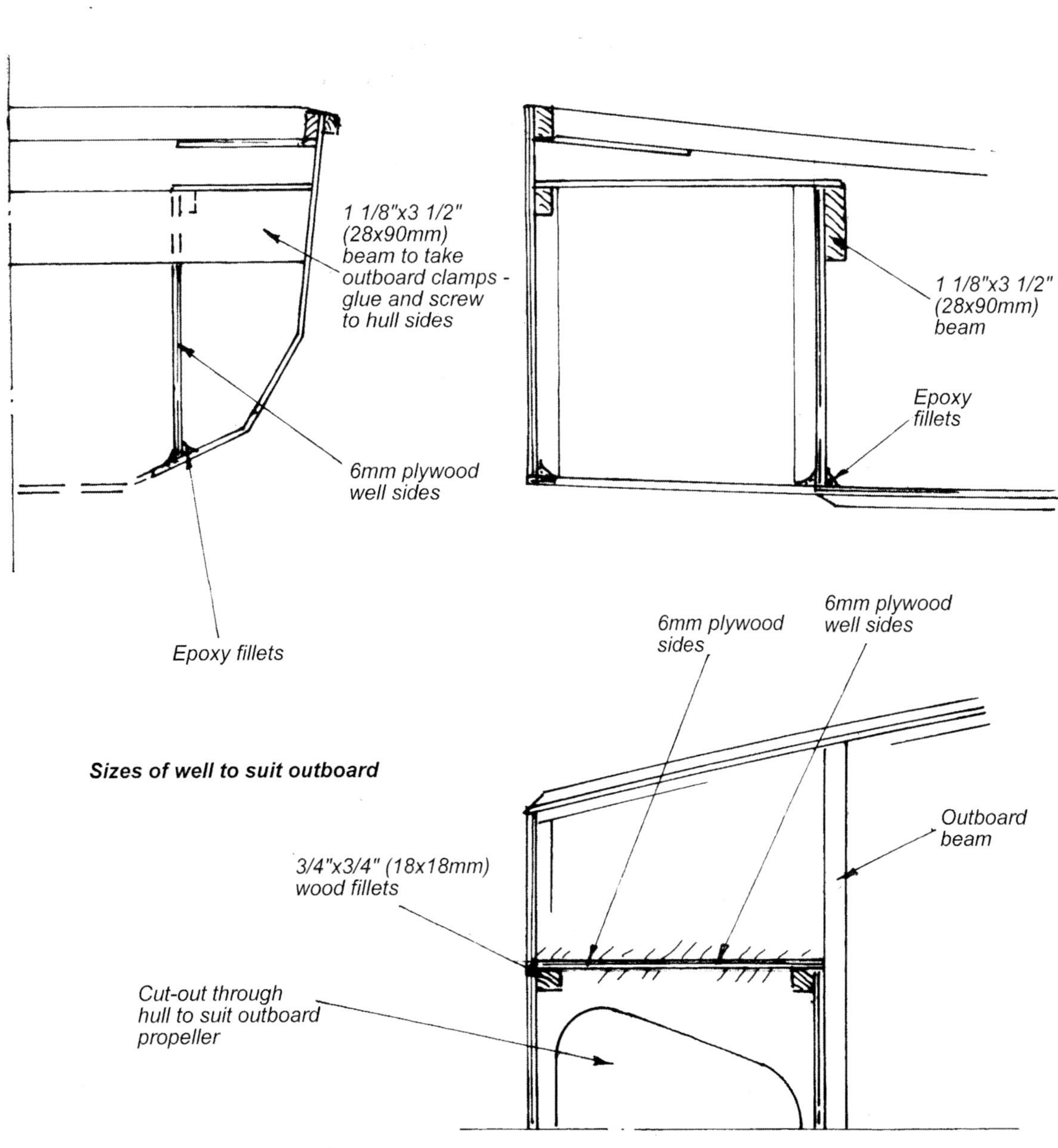

Fig 96. A simple outboard well for a motor canoe.

canoes, but I am often asked about mounting them in a well. Some boaters prefer to mount their outboard in a well because the outboard is more protected and also does not look so bad as it does, hanging off the stern of the boat. However outboard wells remove some of the natural buoyancy gained by the hull shape right aft which means that the boat has less holding it up in this region. So normally, I try to discourage the use of a well on a canoe. A well can be used on a motor canoe with less negative effect because these canoes are designed with more volume/buoyancy aft.

Be careful mounting too powerful an outboard in a well—you can end up with a great rooster tail of water shooting up the well and into the canoe! Figure 96 shows a simple arrangement for use in a motor canoe incorporating some aft decking which could be enclosed top form lockers and stowage aft. Alter the size of the outboard well box to suit your outboard.

Above—a Waterman 16 fitted with a simple box outboard well by Renier Bramley—note the fore and aft seating box which convenient for fishing and storing gear.

12.6 Yokes & Stretchers

A stretcher is simply a piece of wood which keeps the gunwales apart and provides stiffness to the top of the canoe. They are not always needed but often form a handy device to help carry/portage the canoe around locks etc.—see 4.7 on Page 47.

On smaller personal lightweight canoes, the method of carrying the canoe is often akin to wearing a large banana shaped hat with the the canoe upside down, you head in the inverted canoe and the stretcher resting across your shoulders. Carrying a canoe this way leaves your hands more or less free to carry the paddle plus your lunch or some dry cloths, but can get uncomfortable quickly.

The weight on your shoulders can be alleviated by taping some thick foam rubber to the stretcher to soften the area in contact with your shoulders and the stretcher itself can be shaped to be more comfortable than the shape of a simple square sectioned piece of wood. If the stretcher is shaped to make life more comfortable when carrying the canoe on your shoulders, it becomes a 'yoke' similar to that used in illustrations of 'Jack & Jill' from the nursery rhyme.

I have seen some beautifully carved and very ornate yokes and you can really go to town to produce one which shows of your wood carving skills. Figure 97 shows a simple design which can be adjusted in shape to suit your own neck and shoulders and which is made up by gluing two pieces of 1"x2" (25x50mm) together.

Securing it to the canoe is shown in Figure 42 but it can be fitted in such a way that it is removable, simply by bolting up through a thickened inwale.

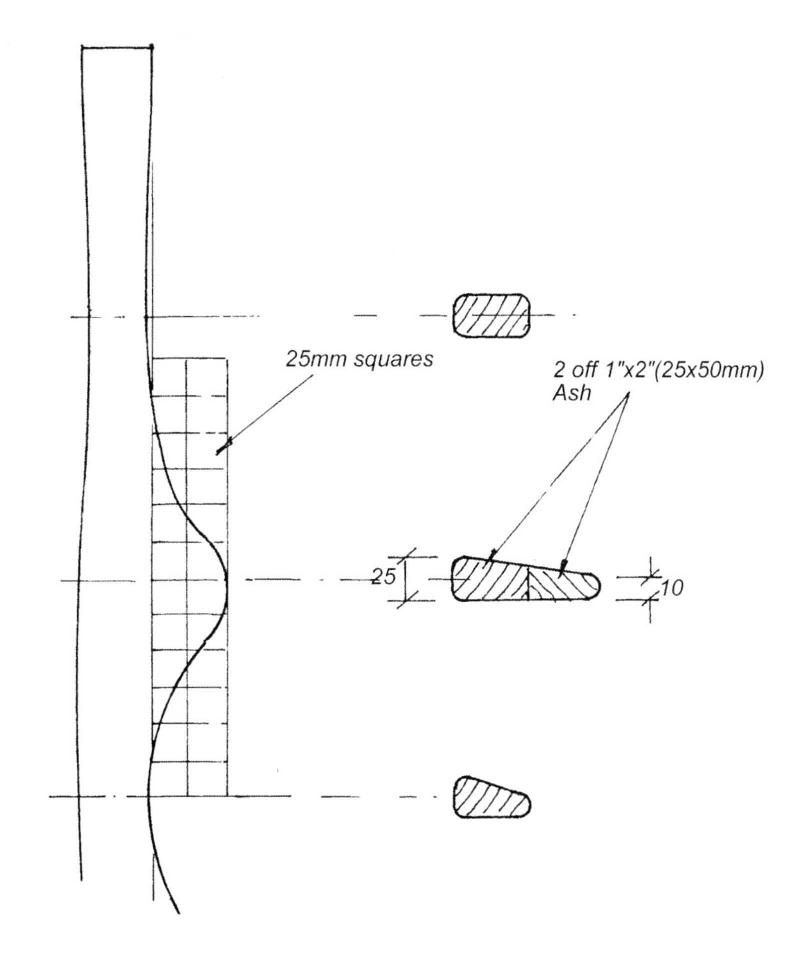

Fig 97. A simple yoke which replaces a stretcher to form a carrying device for the canoe.

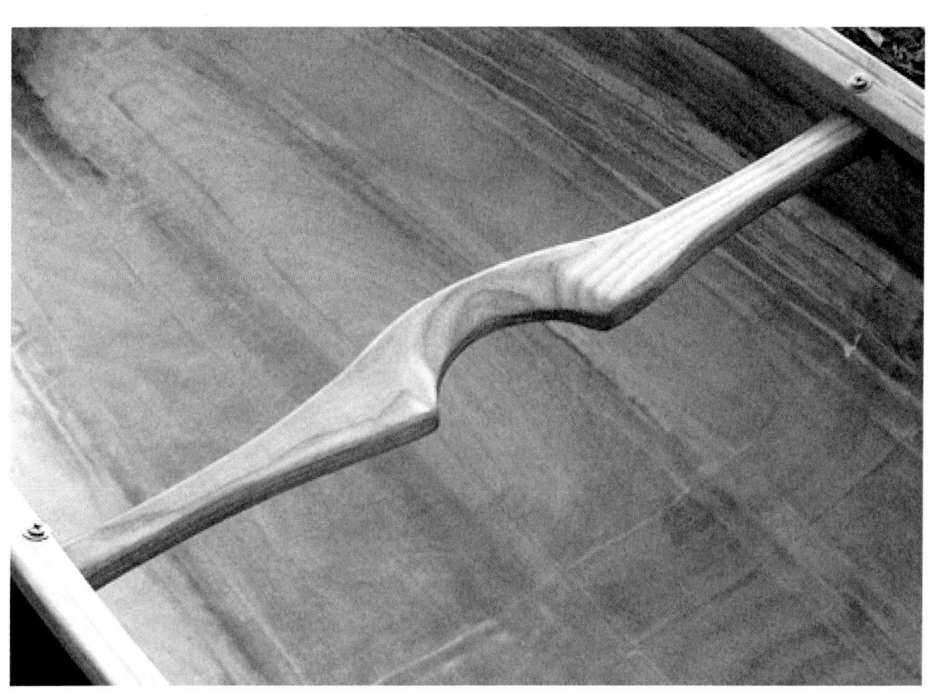

Right—a very nicely shaped yoke fitted to Peterborough 14—not the single bolt through the inwale at each end to fix it into place which is fine for a small canoe.

12.7. Chair/Seat Backs and Bottoms

For some of us oldies, paddling for any length of time can get quite painful especially on the small of the back and having a backrest can be a big help to make canoeing more comfortable. You can buy-in a seat back from a canoe supplier or even, as shown in one of the photographs on this page, use the sort of folding seat backs/bottoms normally fitted to motor boats. If you do use one of these seats do make sure that they do not position your bottom too high as this could upset the stability of the canoe by moving the vertical centre of gravity higher than it should be.

You can build the seat bottoms to have the backs incorporated with them as shown in James Beale's Peterborough 14 or you can make the back to be an 'add-on' which simply slides onto an ordinary flat canoe seat (Figure 98).

Right—Colin Day's Waterman 12 fitted with folding motor boat seats.

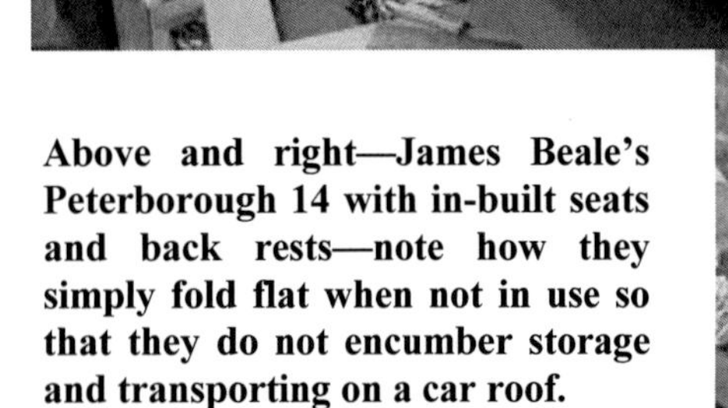

Above and right—James Beale's Peterborough 14 with in-built seats and back rests—note how they simply fold flat when not in use so that they do not encumber storage and transporting on a car roof.

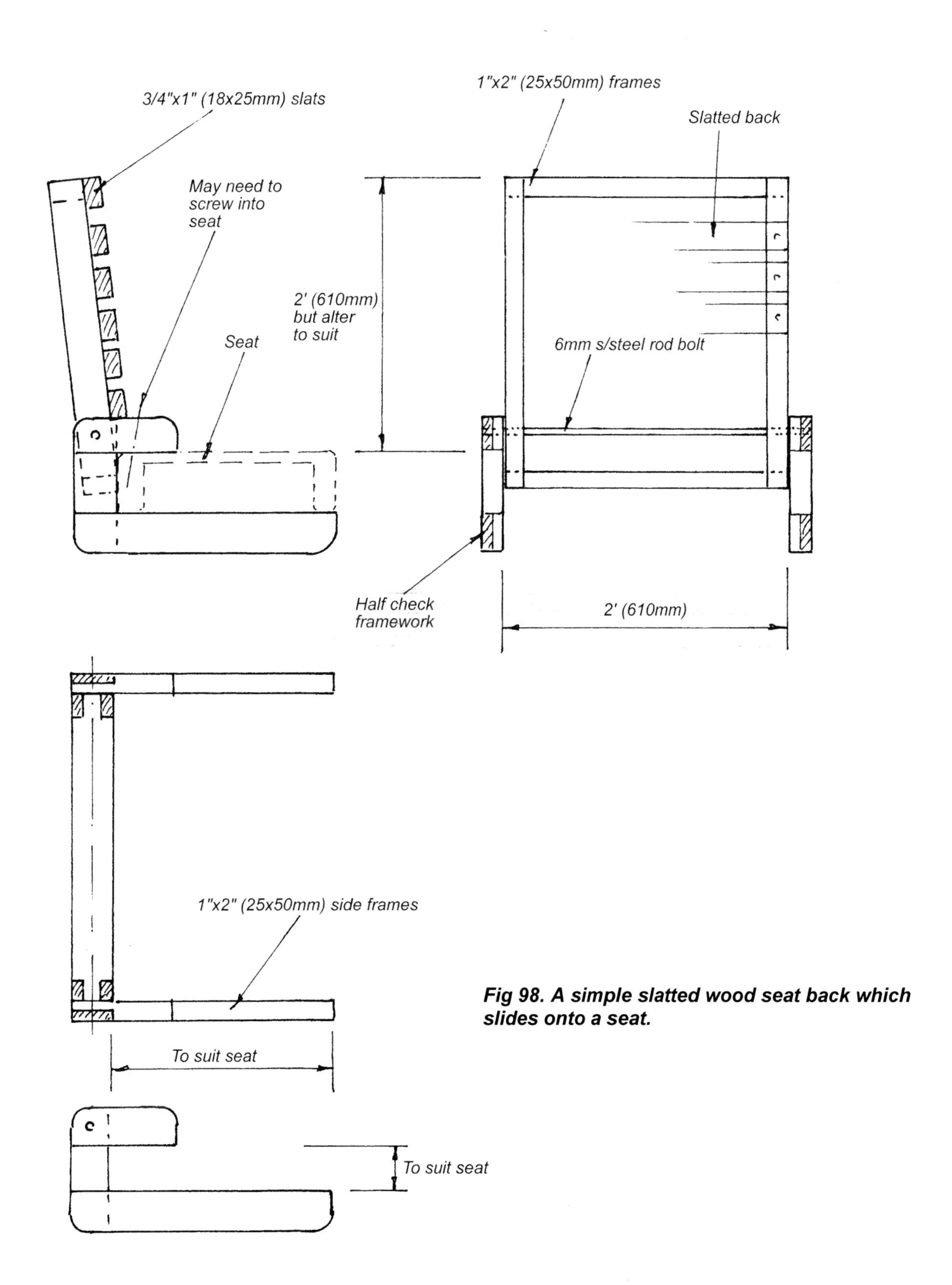

Fig 98. A simple slatted wood seat back which slides onto a seat.

Chapter 8 on Fitting Out the Canoe describes a couple of different seat/thwart bottoms for open canoes but we have not really considered seat bottoms for kayaks.

You can purchase very comfortable seat bottoms for kayaks made from glass fibre or moulded plastic and for their price, they are excellent. Buying one from a canoe store or equipment supplier is often the best way to go but for those wanting to make their own I have shown an example in Figure 99.

You will note that for maximum comfort the shape of the top looking from the side has a lazy 'S' shape with the point of maximum curvature approximately a third of the length back from the front. The length of the seat is often only 13" (330mm) and the width only 12" (305mm) or so to fit in the confined space at the bottom of a kayak but experiment to find the correct size for you.

Rather than going for a curved top the top can be flat and simply slope back. Some of these plywood seats have the top hinging up so that small items can be stored in a box under them.

The curved top would use 1/8" (3mm) ply or 4mm at the most and to get the ply into the shape of the curve, it can be soaked first to make it more supple—the grain of the outer veneers would run from side to side.

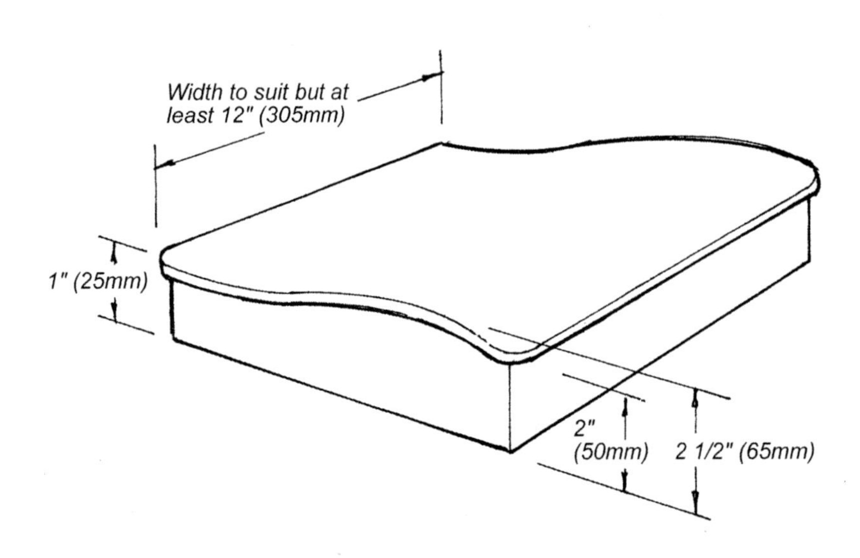

Fig 99. A simple kayak seat.

12.8 Sculling/Rowing Outriggers

Open canoes can make quite successful rowing shells and several Selway Fisher canoes have been used with 'off the shelf' rowing outriggers and sliding seats including the 'FrontRower'. However, many of these specialist systems and rigs are quite expensive.

The problem with rowing a canoe is that the beam is too small to mount rowlocks with enough width between them to allow effective sized oars to be used. The width between rowlocks across the boat wants to be at least 4' (1.22m) and preferably closer to 5' ((1.5m) if possible. Without this width, you either have to use very short oars which are inefficient or cross the looms when rowing which again, is inefficient.

This means that, to get the requisite 4' or so width, the rowlocks need to be mounted on outriggers attached to the gunwales of the canoe. Selway Fisher has the details for metal tube outriggers used on several of our rowing skiff designs but these need to be permanently bolted to the boat which is not what we usually want to do with a canoe—we want a sculling/rowing rig which can be easily removed when not wanted.

Sliding seats require an interior devoid of fixed seats and frames and so, unless you are converting a canoe to be used purely for sculling, it is easier to stick with a fixed seat arrangement.

For most small rowing boats the distance between the aft edge of the rowing seat and the centre of the rowlock wants to be 9-10" (225-250mm).

Figure 100 gives the details for a simple low cost wood arrangement which incorporates a fixed seat with the outriggers. The whole arrangement is designed simply to fit between the gunwales wherever you want to fit it in the canoe so you need to alter the width between the vertical members of the framework, to suit. It will need to be jammed in place or simple chocks can be fitted to the gunwales to keep the athwartships (side to side) parts of the frame work from moving.

The vertical distance of 3 1/2" (90mm) between the top of the plywood seat and the gunwale should not be reduced and if anything, wants to be increased—90mm is the usual height for a canoe seat for paddling but is slightly more than half of what you would normally have on a dinghy seat for rowing.

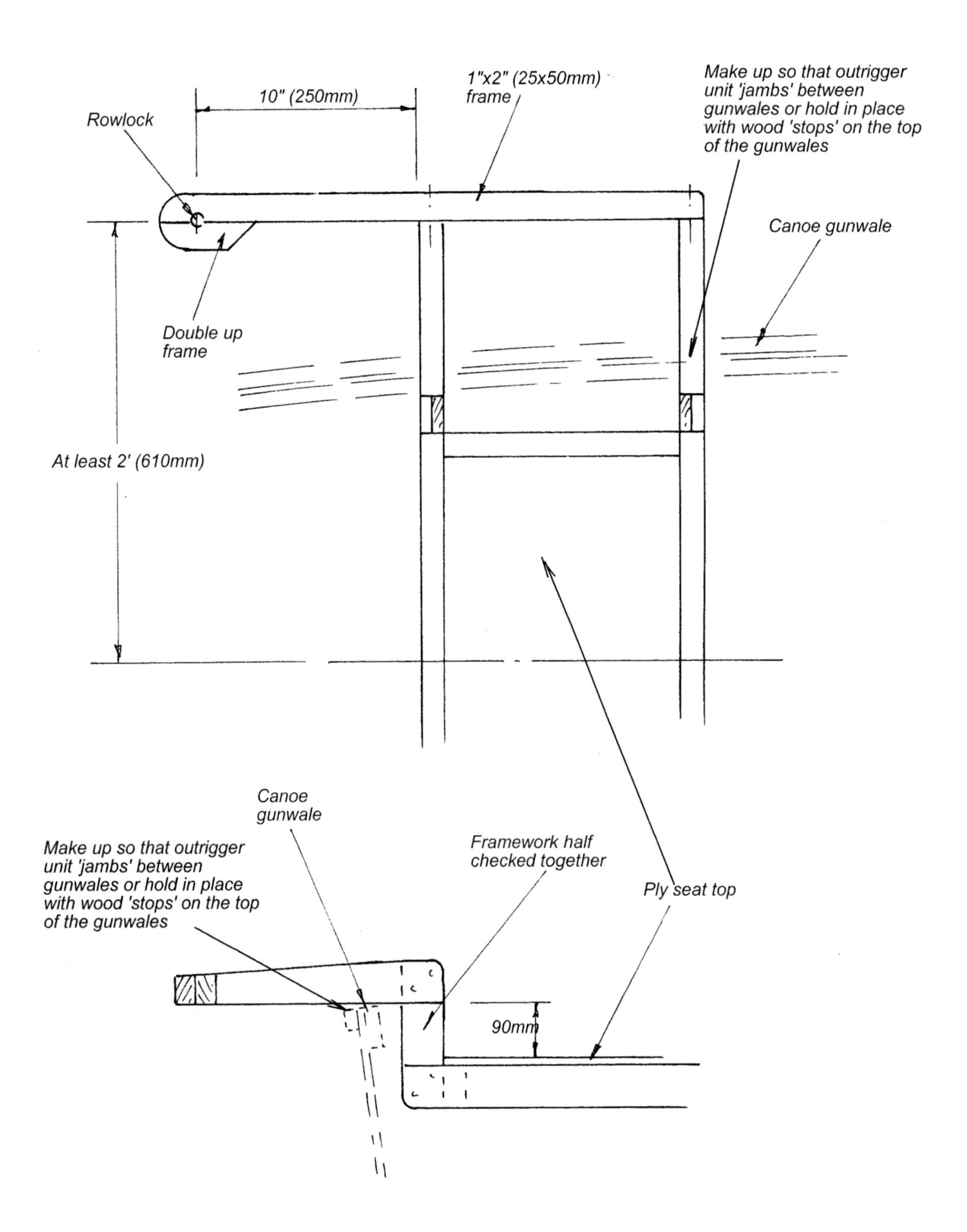

Fig 100. A simple wood sculling outrigger set-up.

12.9 Canoe Trolleys

Again, you can buy a canoe trolley but you can make one with little effort. The trolley I made as a school boy for my PBK 20 double kayak consisted of a wood cross with the keel of the canoe on one piece and the axle attached to the other. This was fine but the wheels had to be well separated or they fouled the hull of the canoe.

A better arrangement is shown in Figure 101. this consists of two wood frames hinged against each other so that the trolley can fold flat. The axle goes through one of the frames and both frames are held the correct distance apart at the top by wide Nylon webbing.

This arrangement gets the canoe up high which means that the framework can be narrower than otherwise needed as the wheels do not foul the canoe itself. Do not make it too narrow though or the canoe will topple to one side—a width of 14" (360mm) for the framework is usually about right. An overall width front to back of 12" (305mm) is good and a length for the longer piece of framework which carries the axle of around 12" (305mm) is also about right—but experiment with these dimensions for your own canoe.

The wheels can be the simple plastic type found in many hobby catalogues and the webbing straps used to secure the canoe to the trolley are the narrow type with jam clasps that you can get from bike shops and car accessory stores.

It is good to have wheels that can easily come off the axle so that the whole arrangement can be stored flat but if not, simply hold them in place with Nyloc nuts or split pins.

The trolley is usually secured to the canoe fairly well aft so that the bow can be picked up when moving the canoe. In past days when there was less and slower traffic on the road, it was quite feasible to attach the bow of the canoe to the back of your bike. I'm not sure that I would do this now and it is probably illegal anyway!

Above—James Beale's 14' Peterborough with a neat and simple canoe trolley designed to be fitted right at the stern of the boat.

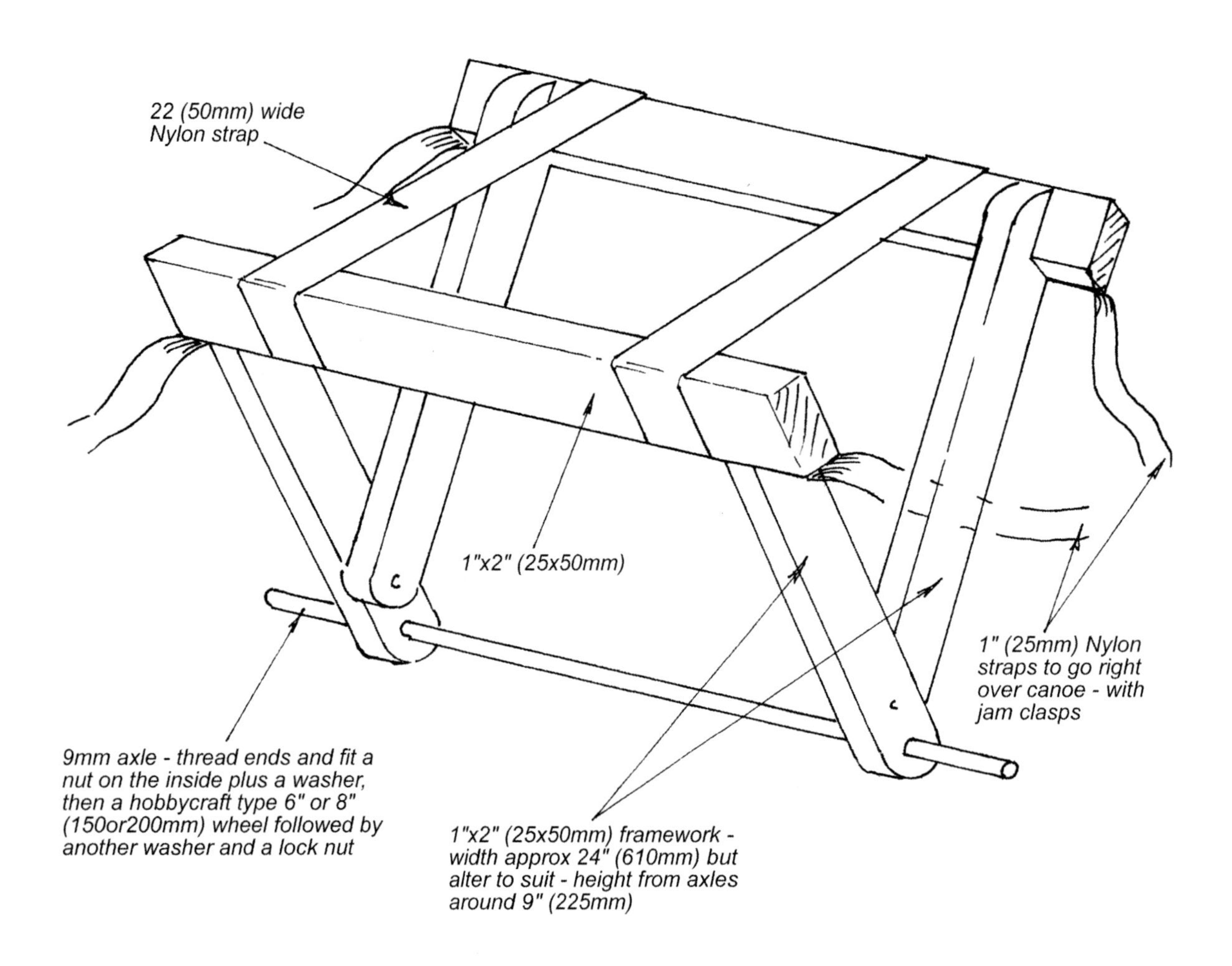

Fig 101. A collapsing canoe trolley.

Chapter 13

APPENDICES

13.1 Cutting Scarf Joins

Often, it is not possible to get pieces of timber long enough to stretch around the canoe for the inwales and outwales etc. It may be that you can get wood sufficiently long enough but have no way of getting it home from the timber yard unless they deliver. When this happens a join needs to be made in the wood to make up the length required and the join we use most often is the simple scarf join—Figure 102.

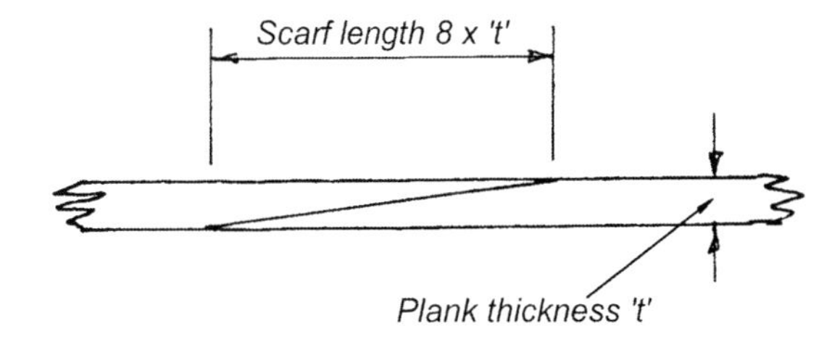

Fig 102. The scarf join.

The scarf consists of cutting a slope onto the ends of each piece and then gluing them together along this scarf. Why a scarf? Well, it is relatively easy to cut and offers a large 'faying' (gluing) area. It is not an 'abrupt' or short join and is therefore a strong joint to use in boat building.

The length of the scarf is usually between 6 and 8 times the thickness of the wood being scarfed and a good scarf can often hardly be seen.

It is a good idea to cut the two ends together so that you get a good match between the two pieces that make up the join—if you mark and cut them separately, you only need to be a millimetre out on the length of one scarf to throw the join out of alignment. There are a couple of ways to do this—Figure 103 shows one method where one piece of wood is laid on top of the other, the scarf line is marked and carried down the front and back faces of both pieces and the two held together in this position to be cut at the same time.

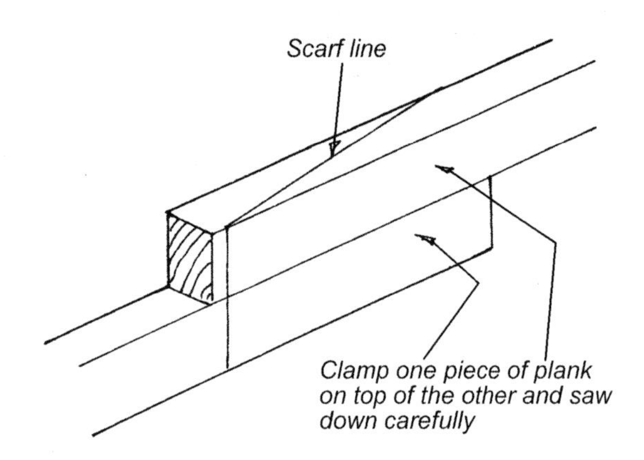

Fig 103. One way of marking and cutting the scarf together on both pieces at the same time.

Another way, especially if the wood is quite small, is to lay the two pieces side by side overlapping each other by twice the length of the scarf, clamp them securely and then mark and cut the scarf whilst the pieces are held in this position.

Above—the two pieces laid side by side and clamped onto a bench—you can see the scarf line has been marked.

Above—cutting the scarf. Use a backed saw (ie. a tenon saw) for this—cut on the line and watch carefully that, as the saw cuts through the pieces of wood, it is held vertically.

Most badly cut joins are caused by the person cutting the join standing too close to the work—this causes the sawing arm to waver and bow—stand well back and make sure that your fore arm stays in-line with the saw as you cut and watch the marked line down the back of the wood to make sure that the saw follows it vertically.

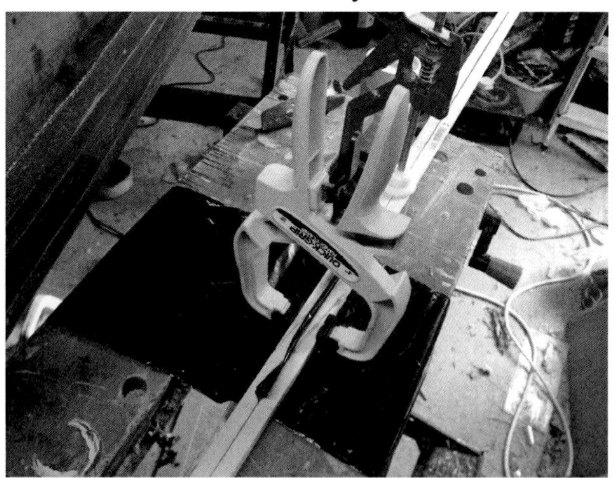

Above—to finish the join, try the pieces together dry and if necessary adjust them with a sharp knife or chisel. You can see that two pieces of outwale are being glued together at the same time—PVC has been laid down on the bench and between the two outwales so that they do not glue where you don't want them too.